DIET

SUPREMACY

The Toxic Bond Between Shame,
Dieting, and Emotional Eating

ROBIN PHIPPS WOODALL

DIET SUPREMACY © 2020 Robin Phipps Woodall.

ISBN: 978-1-7331456-4-0

Printed in the United States of America

Because of the dynamic nature of the Internet, any web addresses or links contained in this book may have changed since publication and may no longer be valid. The views expressed in this work are solely those of the author.

NOTE: Women and men both experience issues stemming from body image, diet, and struggle with emotional eating and eating disorders. For convenience, we primarily used *she/her* throughout.

DISCLAIMER
The author, Robin Phipps Woodall, is not formally trained or educated in psychology, and is not a licensed counselor or therapist. She is not qualified to diagnose and treat eating disorders. However, she does have personal experience suffering with an eating disorder, and with recovery. The author's intent is to share her thoughts, observations, and what she's studied on the matter in hopes that other's might benefit.

Dedication

To the scientists who've dedicated thousands of hours exploring the curiosities and intricacies of the human mind and body—not because they want personal gain, but because they are seeking what is important to humanity. To all of the people who've personally shared their eating disorder experience with me on many levels. They opened up about the truth of their wins and losses, and the vulnerable truth of their struggles. It is their humility and willingness to be honest with me and with themselves that allowed the work I do to evolve.

To the most important people in my life: My husband Mark and my children Chloe, Wyatt, and Suzanne. Thank you for believing in me, and for having patience during the years I couldn't find the energy, motivation, or discipline to get this work done.

Contents

Introduction

My Weight-Loss Apocalypse

"And once the storm is over, you won't remember how you made it through, how you managed to survive. You won't even be sure, whether the storm is really over. But one thing is certain. When you come out of the storm, you won't be the same person who walked in. That's what this storm's all about."

– Japanese writer, Haruki Murakami

How I Got Here…

It's been over twenty years since I miraculously recovered from the grip of a relentless eating disorder and suicidal depression. In a span of three years, I went from being a cheerful, naive, bright-eyed and energetic freshman in college to being severely depressed, mentally ill, and preparing for suicide before the age of 21.

By the second semester of my sophomore year, my life had spiraled out of control as I tried to cope with depression by losing weight. I quickly lost touch with reality as I suffered with an eating disorder that ultimately changed the course of my life. During that time, I gave up a full-ride scholarship, quit school, married a man I only knew for six months, and moved across the country with him. I was in such a dark, emotional pit of despair that during the first year of being married and within months of moving, I decided to commit suicide. However, during a deep state of contemplation as I emotionally prepared to end my life, I miraculously recovered.

> **NOTE:** What promotes an eating disorder is complex. There isn't one thing that causes an eating disorder but rather, I assume that for me it was a combination of factors that together promoted my need to find something to help me survive. A combination of things in my life supported my inclination toward an eating disorder as a coping mechanism. For me, it was strict patriarchal religious beliefs with rigid standards—and how what happened the first years of college—brought on my need to be in control of something, when everything in my life seemed to be irreparably damaged. For whatever reason, I internalized these strict beliefs in such a way that I didn't give myself the forgiveness from my struggles to control my life when objectivity was needed. I couldn't tell the difference between a subjective opinion and reality.

When it comes to other people's stories, and why they might suffer from disordered eating or the severity of an eating disorder, I think it's important to look at it as a collective issue—where separate aspects that come together, and when combined, promote an eating disorder.

Similar to how a "syndrome" is a cluster of symptoms found together, I believe behaviors and thoughts that resemble an eating disorder should be viewed the same way.

Not only did I experience an instantaneous removal from every negative aspect of the disorder and depression, but I also came out of it having a total shift in the way I perceived and lived life.

Afterward, it was discernably clear to me that *the condition of my body was irrelevant as long as it was sufficiently alive to keep me conscious.* The health, leanness, fatness, or attractiveness of my body wasn't important in any way, even if others liked me or disapproved of me because of it. I understood that my body was simply a conduit to experience and express life—and the need to use it to prove myself to others became nonsensical.

I remember afterwards having an intense desire to share my recovery with the world, wanting to shout from the rooftops about the freedom I'd become aware of. But as quickly as I felt the desire to help others, I also felt that my experience might not be meant for others to hear—especially since I didn't quite understand how to explain it. It was a personal experience that felt sacred to me, and I figured that if it were meant to be shared, letting others know about my recovery wouldn't be forced.

There was a sense of peace when I realized that I didn't have to reveal to others what happened, but could peacefully and quietly move on with my life. If the opportunity might arise in the future, then at that point I would share my experience to the best of my ability—but only if it felt appropriate. I didn't tell anyone about my recovery, not even my husband or parents. They were left to witness my recovery without context for why and how it happened. In my mind, it didn't need to be addressed.

After recovering, I began a new life that I directed from a heart-centered and independent state of mind. The first choice I made was to return to the university I left to earn back my scholarship and finish school. To do this I had to face disappointing many people, as well as live apart from my new husband because we would be attending two different schools across the country from each other. Doing so allowed me the time and space to make decisions for myself, and to develop a sense of autonomy and emotional strength.

I finished college with a bachelor's degree in exercise science, and it made sense to carve out a career as a personal trainer. My husband and I started our family, and I worked in the exercise industry for over thirteen years. Today, I am still married to the same man and we now have three children.

Weight-Loss Apocalypse and the Protocol

Ten years later, in 2007 I was approached to help and monitor people through a medical hormonal therapy that required strict adherence to a very low-calorie protocol. This hormonal therapy was created over decades of observation by Dr. A.T.W Simeons, an endocrinologist who studied the pregnancy hormone: Human Chorionic Gonadotropin (hCG). Dr. Simeons' hCG protocol is very controversial because it lacks scientific credibility. However, when I was approached to assist and monitor people going through the protocol, I was fascinated and curious by the physiology of the process. Because I ran my own gym and owned the necessary equipment, I was able to do a variety of tests to monitor the physical response each patient experienced. Over the course of three years, I felt compelled to publish not only the data I collected regarding the physical results of the medical protocol, but also my observations with respect to the emotional aspects of the protocol as it related to weight loss and emotional eating.

Introduction

I thoroughly describe the hormonal protocol, give a hypothesis for how it could work, explain my experience working with patients, as well as present the testing results that I gathered in my first book, *Weight-Loss Apocalypse Book 1,* and in my second book, *Weight-Loss Apocalypse Book-2.*

For years, as I met with clients weekly to do testing, I got to know each person as we'd discuss the details of the medical protocol, their testing results, and the roadblocks they experienced. I came to observe that the measurements and tests I was doing greatly influenced the client's emotions and motivation, and we would end up talking more about their issues with food and the discontent they had with their body than with the actual protocol.

The hardest part of the protocol, despite the potential physical benefits, was getting people to follow it. As much as I approached the hCG protocol as a hormonal therapy for the body, the people doing it were highly emotional about it, as if it was more about proving their worth than it was about improving their health. Most people were doing it as a way to fix their poor self-esteem, which made them emotional about the physical results. I observed that the intentions of the client and the way they viewed the process changed his or her response to both the limitations of the protocol as well as the physical results. Because I believed the client's motivation to follow the protocol was imperative to getting accurate results, as well as a truthful understanding of the potential physical benefits, my interest shifted from the physiology of the process to the emotional aspects that made it difficult for people to follow the protocol. I observed that when people were emotional about the weight loss, they struggled: To discern physical hunger and satiation, making the protocol very difficult for them to follow.

- With obsessive monitoring of their size and weight. How they reacted to the change directly impacted their willingness to follow the protocol.

- With emotional desires to eat. They'd reason and rationalize not adhering to the protocol despite not being hungry and risking the potential physical benefits the protocol could provide.

- To accept the natural results of the protocol, despite significant physical improvements.

- With fear about weight gain and reintroducing food once the protocol was over, making them increasingly obsessed with their weight and food.

- With increased emotional eating and binge eating the more they feared food after the protocol was over.

I found that my past experience with an eating disorder and my miraculous recovery kept coming up as I'd recognize how they were feeling and how that impacted their relationship with food. It was as if I was witnessing my past thoughts, impulses, and behavior in some variation in every person I observed. As I met with each person and his or her issues would arise, I'd attempt to give them insight based on the recollection of my own recovery, and it would help.

This was very difficult because I'd put my disorder and recovery on a shelf—and to help others I had to bring it all back up to the forefront of my mind. These were things I hadn't thought about in over a decade. To me, it was a past life that didn't need to be processed, rethought, or discussed. I was free, and had no reason to rehash my previous disorder and recovery. However, the more I interacted with patients through the medical protocol, the more my previous suffering and recovery came up.

Because I could relate, I could help verbalize much of what they were experiencing, whereas by themselves they didn't have words to describe or explain it.

Introduction

Weight-Loss Apocalypse and YouTube Sessions

As I met with more and more people, I found that the issues they struggled with became more and more predictable. As well, some common roadblocks and questions consistently came up. To answer these questions and to show how I coached people through roadblocks, I started a YouTube channel. Through videos, I shared with followers the process I describe in *Weight-Loss Apocalypse, Books 1 and 2*. I posted full sessions showing me talking with clients as I prepared them for the hCG protocol, as well as follow-up sessions discussing roadblocks and emotional issues with food and their body.

My experience with an eating disorder came up consistently as I tried to help explain what I was observing in these clients. Over the course of a couple of years, people from all over the globe found my YouTube channel and started reaching out for my help. Gradually, as the clients struggled with more intense issues, the content of my posted sessions shifted away from the hCG protocol to being focused on emotional eating, body image, the diet industry, and eating disorders.

Today I've helped hundreds of people from all over the world who have suffered with issues from across the spectrum of eating disorders.

As more and more people diagnosed with eating disorders reached out to me to talk, the more I've been challenged to understand my own recovery.

I've had to revisit my past trauma, past depression, and the darkness of the eating disorder I was trapped by in order to be able to help others express and describe what they are experiencing. I've also had to recall my own recovery, and to find words to explain and give context to what I experienced. It has taken me years working with hundreds of people, as well as countless hours studying, to have a bigger grasp on the issue that goes beyond my own personal experience, and even today, I struggle to communicate it properly.

In 2019, I published my full story in *My Weight-Loss Apocalypse: Rebirth from the Ashes of Eating Disorder Hell.* My story is available to purchase from my website at: https://WeightLossApocalypse.com

You will find throughout the *Thin-Supremacy* series of books that I reference my experience with an eating disorder, as well as my recovery. It is very difficult to explain what it feels like, and the way a person thinks when they have an eating disorder, unless you have fully recovered. This is why I consistently describe my experience and use myself as an example. It can help the reader find a sense of understanding, get relief and be able to relate.

My hope when I published *My Weight-Loss Apocalypse* was to describe my story and to give people context for where my awareness of eating disorders come from. Again, I am not a licensed therapist, nor am I formally trained in psychology in any way. Outside of a dietetics course specific to eating disorders I took one semester in college, my knowledge about the subject comes from personal experience, research, lots of reading, and from the observations I've made talking to people who've sought out my feedback.

My goal in writing the *Thin Supremacy* series of books is to give those that connect with the content of my YouTube sessions more important information that might make sense of the work I'm doing. *If you are suffering from an eating disorder, but don't connect to the content I present, it probably isn't appropriate for your condition.* You should seek out help that is appropriate, and that offers you relief. Don't give up! There is sense in why you're suffering; you just need to find the reasons and seek out answers for what needs to change in order to bring you peace.

For those that connect, all I can give is insight. I don't have exact instructions. What I present here are my thoughts and what I've studied about the subject. These are my subjective observations, and if they help, great!

My hope is that eating disorders are looked at from a new angle, not as a disorder, but as a syndrome. My intent is to openly discuss the issues from a broader perspective, and to give insight to people that might help, in some way, to relieve their suffering. I don't promise recovery, but rather to open your mind and give you hope. Permanent recovery is possible. You might need to look at things differently, and that's what I hope to do: *to give you a different perspective.*

The Goals of the *Thin Supremacy* Book Series

These books were written for people struggling with issues stemming from body image, dieting, emotional eating, and eating disorders, and for professionals who help people suffering with these issues. *These books are not light reading.* The content and information presented is meant to help the reader to see things from a different point of view. For this to happen, you might need to read, study, cross reference, and reread different chapters from each book in the series. From a change in perspective, the goal is to see from a larger vantage point, to think differently, and to ask questions that might have uncomfortable answers.

If you are looking for light-hearted easy reading, these books are not for you.

Thin Supremacy focuses and discusses the underlying psychological mechanisms and societal belief systems that reinforce a culture that encourages them to battle their weight.

Diet Supremacy focuses on the survival mechanisms that are triggered as this struggle to accept body fat promotes an anxiety-ridden conflict between dieting—and the survival urges to gain access to food and to eat in self-defense.

Body Supremacy presents a method of recovery from the culture of thin supremacy, and from the toxic war between dieting and emotional eating. This book gives the reader a look into what recovery feels like, and sends a message of hope to those who are seeking freedom from an eating disorder.

Life After Supremacy goes deeper into the mind and darkness of eating disorders. This book discusses the possibility that eating disorders might be more of a syndrome, where compliance is a form of self-preservation necessary to survive in narcissistic cultures where codependency and trauma bonding might be more prevalent.

SECTION 1

The Body Image Mirage

*"Until you make the unconscious conscious,
it will direct your life and you will call it fate."*

– Carl Jung

Chapter 1

Tug-of-War Between Weight Lost and Weight Gained

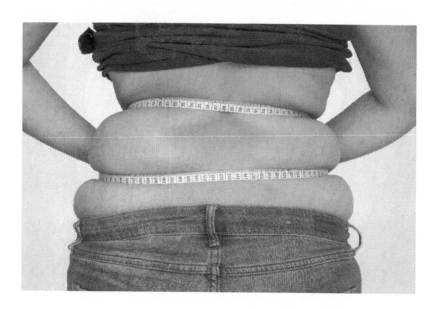

"Diets are essentially training courses in how to feel fat and feel like a failure."

– Paul McKenna, Life Coach and Author

Feeling Like a Failure

There's always an awkward moment after someone asks me what I do for a living. I'm not sure what to tell them, and I'm not sure they'll understand. Usually I try to avoid bringing the medical weight-loss program I've studied (and become an expert at) into the conversation and simply answer that I help people with emotional eating and body-image issues.

Discussing weight loss is complicated, and so is the topic of emotional eating and body image. Most are initially surprised that I'm associated with a medical treatment that requires very rigid food restrictions, chiefly since my primary work is helping people recover with body-image issues and emotional complications people have with eating because of dieting. It seems counterintuitive to be supportive of both.

They frequently say, "I know this one lady who lost a lot of weight. But she's gained it all back, and I don't see her out much anymore. I know another woman who seems to be dieting and battling her weight year-round. She's trying a new diet every time I talk to her."

The general view of people who chronically diet, or struggle to keep off fat they made great effort to lose is that something must be wrong. The people who've lived their lives this way, dieting over and over again, and finding it almost impossible to manage weight loss and weight gain—probably would agree.

The truth is, there is something that isn't working, and it is likely promoting a person's sensitivity to fat gain. The food you eat, when you eat, and how you eat, as well as your metabolism, emotional eating, toxins in your environment, and stress in your life, have all been looked at as contributing factors. However, there is a large body of evidence that suggests judgment, shame, fear, and negative attitudes about body fat have a direct and significant impact on both the follower's psychological drive to eat excessively and her physical sensitivities that promote fat gain.

> **In other words, for those who believe it, body fat judgment and stigma increases their personal likelihood of becoming and remaining obese. The belief in the "badness' of obesity alone increases your risks.** [1, 2, 3]

Without this knowledge, people are blind to the big picture, and can see only the end result of growing body fat as the problem.

Nearly half (45%) of the people in the United States remain worried about their weight "all" or "some of the time."[39] That's a huge portion of the population who fear his or her own body, and most of those people are women.[39] As these people sacrifice food and diet in an effort to fix the fat they deem is problematic, within 1 to 5 years about 95% of them will regain any fat they had lost.

In the end, the more that people try to lose the body fat they're worried about, the more weight they inevitably regain. A person internalize that failure, feeling worse about herself and the fat she can't seem to get rid of.

Consider how that must feel—putting in the time, thought, expense, and effort—and the results are nothing more than a mirage. How can this not negatively impact a dieter's relationship with food?

> **The natural assumption for a dieter is to think 1) he or she must not have what it takes, which is an indication of personal incompetence, or 2) that diets suck.**

As the weight-loss industry blames food as the problem, they perpetually churn out and reintroduce "new and improved" ways to get rid of the "bad" fat that they want you to be afraid of. A dieter continues to worry about her weight and continues to wait for the next best dieting formula to emerge so she can try again.

Email requesting my help from 20-year-old female:
"I started to diet with my friends when I was 16 years old. It was the healthy thing to do and I wanted to fit in. I haven't been "normal" with food since.

I don't really know how to be normal with food anymore, and I can't imagine eating carbs and sugars without guilt or feeling like I've ruined everything. This is the first time I've ever said this to anyone, but I think dieting this way has led to an eating disorder. Every time I eat bad food I think, "What's the point. I already messed up, so I might as well eat everything I want today." Back then, I'd eat crazy amounts of food all day and try to diet the next day. But for the past couple of years things have gotten much worse. I started eating so much that I got sick, and then I made myself throw it up so I could relieve the pain. Now I make myself puke intentionally.

I didn't think it was anything serious at first because it was an easy way to cheat on my diet. But it's became a regular behavior. To start I did this every couple of months, then once a month, one a weekend, and now every single day. I overeat, puke, and go back on the diet.

I've been having more stress lately, and I've been intentionally overeating in order to deal with it, knowing I have a way to get rid of the shame of cheating on my diet. It seemed like an easy way to not gain weight, and to also get to eat like a normal person. I see now this is the furthest thing from normal! I was at 142 pounds, but now I've gained 15 pounds and I feel horrible. I have insanely low self-image.

22

I'm terrified I won't be able to get back to 142 pounds because I can't seem to stick to low carb and no sugar, especially since I've become reliant on puking. I AM MISERABLE. This has taken over my life. I have acknowledged that this is a serious problem. I need some advice. Anything. I really want to change my ways on my own, but I clearly don't know how to stop."

Readers: What part of her experience resonates with you?

1. Did you start dieting because you thought it was healthy?
2. Did you start dieting because you thought it was healthy?
3. Have you forgotten how to be "normal" around food?
4. When you eat "bad" food do you feel like you've done something wrong? Do you experience guilt?
5. If you purge, when you first started to puke after eating, did you think it wasn't a big deal?
6. Once you started purging, did you notice binges got bigger and occurred more often?

Do Diets Work?

When you ask dieters who've "battled their weight" for a large portion of their life how much fat they've lost, when they add together all weight lost over time, most estimate over 1,000 pounds. Clients who've dieted for over 50 years estimate that they've lost combined over 2,000 pounds.

That's a lot of successful weight-loss methods.

Unfortunately, when a person describes having lost 1,000-2,000 pounds over decades of dieting, he or she is also describing having gained that much fat—and more.

Typically, when people say diets don't work, they aren't talking about the capacity for the body to lose fat. They are talking about the fact that what it takes to lose weight can't be realistically enforced all the time, and ultimately weight lost turns into weight gained. The food-restrictive methods people put themselves through to lose weight commonly backfire, resulting in weight lost that is regained.

> **Important reminder:** There is a large body of evidence that suggests judgment, shame, fear, and negative attitudes about body fat have a direct and significant impact on believer's psychological drive to eat excessively and physical sensitivities that promote fat gain.

> **For those who are certain of it, body fat judgment and stigma increases their personal likelihood of becoming and remaining obese. The worry about weight and the belief in the "badness" of obesity alone increases their susceptibility to gaining more fat.** [1,2,3]

For many people, years of chronic off-and-on again dieting brings to any weight-loss program, feelings of emotional hardship with their body and a history of resentments for having been deprived of food over and over again.

Old grudges, like having to control or limit food as a child, are projected onto the diet. Consequently, no matter how promising and healing a weight-loss program is physically, the resentment for having to restrict food or exercise to exhaustion in order to receive someone else's approval, makes any method of wight loss feel like a weapon or a sick form of punishment.

> **When a diet is done to lose weight in order to gain another's approval, it is easy to feel burdened—and breaking the rules of**

the food restrictions would be a foreseeable form of self-defense, retribution, and retaliation, even though it hurts only the body the participant is trying to fix.

And once the participant starts deviating from the food restrictions, she can make the entire weight-loss program an all-or-nothing ordeal. The next thing she knows, she's completely quit a few days or a couple weeks into her program, thinking the next time she'll have more willpower which will make dieting easier.

There's always the mirage that a future weight-loss program will work.

If the next program does work and weight is lost again, any excitement or pride can backfire, showing itself as exaggerated fear of weight gain when the process is over. Regrettably, the paranoia of regaining body fat that you just lost impacts how you relate to food in such a way that you'll experience anxiety when you eat, as if food is the enemy and a dangerous threat to your hard-earned success.

As a result, people assume stricter and more perfectionistic food restrictions are needed as a "lifestyle" form of insulation from temptation and as permanent fat-gain protection. This approach to food tends to be unrealistic—often requiring a person to isolate herself from pleasurable foods and social engagement. As a result, the urge to eat emotionally intensifies.

The more pressure a dieter feels to continuously restrict food as she loses body fat, the more likely it is that she'll experience emotional and physical cravings for food, and ultimately, the more likely that she'll eventually overeat.

The problem is that the emotional intensity that goes into reaching unrealistic fat-loss expectations project an intensity onto a diet's restrictions.

This comes across in the mind as anxiety, tension, or "stress" that increases the pressure for him or her to restrict perfectly, which promotes an unforgiving all-or-nothing approach to enforcing the diet. If there is one deviation or misstep, even if it's minor, the dieter's mind equates it to complete failure, which increases his or her risk of bingeing while trying to enforce food restrictions. Or they might just quit mid-way, thinking that without perfection and the most amount of fat loss possible, finishing the program isn't worth it—despite the weight-loss already earned.

The more emotionally rewarding the weight loss is, the less a person is realistic about her ability to follow a diet's food restrictions. The more she inflates her ability to adhere to strict diets and exercise routines, the more likely she is to struggle and quit when the truth sets in.

People who want to remove the image of being seen as "bad" end up "over dieting," which typically results in overeating, and the consequential fat gain is discriminately listed as the problem.

NOTE: As the desire to eat increases, the need for weight and size loss as motivation becomes magnified in a dieter's mind. It's common that when a diet feels hard, the individual might fastidiously weigh herself multiple times a day, body checking, and scrupulously tracking her shape with fanatical measures.

This type of emotional reactivity and impulsiveness might be an indication of deeper problems, like disordered eating or an eating disorder that the weight-loss method might be exaggerating. A high level of emotional strain with the body projects a high level of strain onto food restrictions, and puts a ton of emotional pressure on the weight-loss aspects of a diet—and this is an indication that the participant might need help with body-image issues or help from a licensed therapist.

Weight-loss program participants find they begin to have more disordered eating behaviors after having attempted more and more restrictive dieting lifestyles over and over again, thinking that's what they need to do to be "healthy."

Ultimately, any significant amount of fat loss returns—and so does shame for not being able to maintain those losses. The cyclical tug-of-war between weight lost and weight gained continues.

Emotional Dieting

Over the last ten years while observing people of all walks of life diet and attempt different methods of weight loss, I've witnessed that the more negative someone is about his or her body fat, the more difficulty, stress, and behavioral conflict is experienced during and after their weight-loss program.

The reasons people want to lose weight, and the emotional pressure they bring to a weight-loss program, can make any weight-loss program stressful. Even if the participants are mentally prepared and have a realistic outlook, most people will continue to hope (and expect) for what they are fantasizing weight loss will do for them emotionally.

Unfortunately, most people attempt weight-loss programs because they want to:
- Feel better about themselves,
- Feel better about how they present themselves publicly,
- Prove they have value to society,
- Lose weight to feel pride of their wedding pictures, or
- To feel attractive enough to get out on the dating scene.
- Remove fear and anxiety about their "unhealth."
- Etc.

The context for why you want to lose body fat has the power to

make or break the long-term outcome of a weight-loss program's results, and ultimately should be evaluated prior to attempting a food-restrictive program.

However, because weight-loss businesses promote unrealistic images that specifically appeal to the consumer's emotional fantasies and needs to be thinner, without addressing the negative stress they have about their body, people continue to approach diets with the same strain and pressure, and ultimately have the same sensitivity to fat gain, and resulting urges to emotionally eat when it's over.

Message from woman in her 30's:
Hi Robin, I have been watching your YouTube videos and all I can say is WOW! I have been struggling with body image since I was 6 years old; I am 33 now.

I have been to many healers, psychologist, psychiatrists, etc. In fact, I studied counseling and social science myself. I have not come across anyone that has truly healed themselves and been able to exit this "cult mentality," doing like you have.

I experienced relief from binge eating and my anorexic tendencies when I found the raw vegan lifestyle. This taught me how to eat when I am hungry and to nourish my body with wholesome food. But I'm no longer a raw vegan because even that lead me to obsessive orthorexia. I still struggle though with the mental aspects of body image as I continue in the mental trap of wanting to lose weight, even though I no longer diet or restrict physically. Mentally there is a tug of war going on, I am not overweight at all, but in my mind, I need to be leaner and drop at least 5 kgs (11 lbs.). I am challenging this notion and feel like I could do with your expertise. I live in Australia (Melbourne).

Readers: What part of her experience resonates with you?

1. Have you spent your childhood, teenage, and adult years worried about your body?
2. Have you sought therapy, help, and education from every possible source?
3. Has your eating disorder transferred from one disorder to the next? From binge eating disorder, to orthorexia? From anorexia, to bulimia?
4. Are you obsessed with health, in hopes you'll lose weight or stay thinner?

The Fantasy of Weight Loss and Emotional Drive to Diet

Every single person who reaches out for my help has some emotional expectation she imagines fat loss will give her, with attached symbolism in her mind about what being thinner will do for her. Whether it's a life without knee pain, a concept of health she's been sold, a more self-confident experience at the beach, a perfectly fitting wedding dress, proof that she still has her youth when she turns forty-five, earned pride from her mother when she sees her slimmer, superiority for quickly losing post-baby body fat, having done something better than her sister, or keeping her spouse from cheating again. All of these goals symbolize something imagined in his or her mind, that has a halo around it or degree of fantasy.

As described in more detail in *Thin Supremacy:*

- The worship of thinness attaches positive symbolism to weight loss.

- The emotional attachment that people commonly associate

to weight loss is love, pride, confidence, security, safety, and freedom.

- The idea of being leaner and thinner is symbolized with hard work, determination, education, will power, acceptance, approval, health, achievement, success, and worth.

- In cultures that promote superior body images of thinness, having more fat symbolizes laziness, stupidity, and inferiority.

- People generally attach emotions of sadness, anger, and embarrassment to the way they perceive their body in relation to their size and weight.

- For many people, weight loss is also associated with feelings of anxiety, pressure, perfectionism, isolation, paranoia, and fear of regaining the weight.

In a culture that thinks this way, it makes sense why people would feel bad about their bodies and be at war with their weight. They aren't just worried about their health—they're worried about public humiliation.

These symbolic reasons are why people become attracted to weight-loss programs and medical treatments that are more extreme. All attention focuses on how to get rid of the fat we stigmatize, instead of questioning the logic behind the judgments. People try the next best weight-loss method without adjusting their viewpoint to see the impact that feeling bad about themselves and about dieting has had on their self-preservation with food. They do the same thing over and over again without questioning the fundamental reasons why they are drawn to that cycle in the first place.

Because negative beliefs about body fat are why people are drawn to restrict food in the first place, I believe it's important to repeat, again: there is a large body of evidence that suggests judgment, shame, fear, and negative attitudes about body fat have a direct and significant impact on believer's psychological drive to eat excessively and physical sensitivities that promote fat gain.

For those who are convinced it's true, body fat judgment and stigma increases their personal likelihood of becoming and remaining obese. The worry about weight and the belief in the "badness' of obesity alone increases your physical sensitivity to fat gain. [1,2,3]

Request for my help from a woman in her 20's:
I need help with emotional eating. I am purposely overeating and gaining weight. I am isolating myself right now and am afraid of vulnerability. I've been pretty healthy my entire life except the past two years. Now I find myself bingeing for months; then going on extreme diets to lose a lot of weight fast. I have no consistency anymore. I once had a well-balanced diet, now I am a yo-yo dieter and exercise off and on. Can you help me become consistent again and stop jumping from one extreme to the next?

Readers: What part of her experience resonates with you?

1. Were you normal as it relates to food for a long time, but found that eating for emotional reasons has changed your relationship with food?
2. Have you lost your confidence and feel overwhelmed with life?

3. Are you intentionally overeating to cope with insecurities, knowing that at some point you'll feel stronger and later can restrict food to lose the weight?

4. When you want freedom from restrictions in order to eat food for emotional or social reasons, do you exercise more so you don't have to diet to prevent weight gain?

Ask yourself:

✓ Are you worried about having too much body fat?

✓ Have you experienced shame, judgment, and rejection because of your body?

✓ How did that impact your personal sense of value?

✓ Have you experienced social anxiety and distress because of fears about your body?

✓ Were you more accepted and liked because of the way your body looked?

✓ What are the symbolisms you've attached to being thinner?

✓ How much weight lost have you accumulated over the course of trying to be thinner?

✓ How much have you regained?

✓ If body image was removed from the way you define your worth, how would that impact your life?

✓ Would you voluntarily diet if weight loss wasn't a possibility?

✓ How many times have you consciously accepted weight gain, thinking that someday you'd lose that weight again, and more?

Chapter 2

Surviving the Dogma of Thin Supremacy

"Don't be afraid of losing people. Be afraid of losing yourself by trying to please everyone around you."

– Author Unknown

The topic of body image is very complex. For this reason, I've dedicated the entire book of *Thin Supremacy* to this discussion. In order to fully grasp the links between the desire to lose weight, dieting, and resultant disordered eating behaviors, it's imperative I discuss body image here. In this chapter, I've copied and condensed parts of what's written in *Thin Supremacy* in order to remind the reader why the link between thin(ner)-supremacy body images and resultant emotional eating problems is so important.

> **NOTE:** You might want to skip this chapter or come back to it later, but either way this discussion of how body image represents survival is imperative when trying to understand resultant emotional eating, disordered eating, and the intensity of eating disorders.

What is Body Image?

The traditional understanding of body image is that it is an internalized mental image of the body a person identifies by and wants, typically represented by what is perceived as safe or seen positively by others. *The idea is that a positively seen body reflects a positive inner-self.* It's as though the state of the body—its function, its looks, and other people's opinion about it—symbolizes safety from death and our value as a human, and can then be used to identify the quality and character of the person we are.

Thus, we are led to maintain and uphold:

> **If your body is praised, it's because your body is superior… making you superior. If your body is criticized, it's because your body is inferior…making you inferior.**

Ultimately, a superior body represents freedom from misery and death. Many people I work with describe feeling detached from their body, as if they can't inhabit it until it is "good enough." The goal they are chasing is to get their body to a predetermined state that they think when it's achieved, it will open life up to be lived in—safe from judgment, ridicule, and abandonment.

For a person to achieve that physical state, she must first internalize a concept of what determines right and correct in her mind, to which she agrees with and then compares her body to. That comparison dictates how she defines her relationship with her body in a positive or negative way, and then concludes if it's safe to be inhabited and accepted. It's a matter of conforming the body to a suitable image that "fits in" to the world she wants freedom to live in.

Today, the superior state of the body most people are pursuing is one that has minimal body fat. Over the past few generations, body-image standards of leanness have become so ingrained as being "unquestionable truth" that no one questions their validity. Worshipping and promoting the thinner ideal has become dogmatic.

> **NOTE:** *Dogma is a firm belief, or a set of beliefs, given by an authority, which are promoted as doctrine not to be questioned.* When dogma is internalized, it becomes fact in one's mind, as if it is his or her own personal belief. It becomes sacred truth that acts like an unseen anchor from which all direction is limited and constrained by. Although, in the case of dogma, it isn't a literal anchor but rather an emotional anchor constraining, with bias, the thoughts, perception, and behavior of those who internalize it.
>
> Once a dogmatic belief is internalized as safe and credible, there is no need to look at it, question it, or even suggest it is problematic. Particularly if it's perceived as sacred authority or as superior truth from which evaluations, judgments, and conclusions are drawn.

The belief is that you should persist to be thinner than you naturally are, even if being super thin isn't realistic for your body. No matter how much weight you've lost, you could still lose more. Even if it is only five more pounds—you aren't thin enough.

I call this dogma "thin supremacy," or "thinner supremacy,"
that is: no matter what, *you could always be thinner, and thin-*
ner is always better.

IMPORTANT: For most people the goal isn't necessarily to be thin, but rather they'd like to be thinner than they are. *For this reason, I refer to thin supremacy as thin(ner) supremacy.*

There are other forms of body-image supremacy, like:

- Health supremacy
- Fitness supremacy
- Athletic supremacy
- Sexual-Purity supremacy
- Sexual-Attractive supremacy
- Hair supremacy
- Etc.

Today, the predictable body images that people compare their bodies to are marketed by businesses that profit from selling concepts of safety through health and fitness, as well as concepts of inclusion through sexual attractiveness and beauty. These concepts are repeatedly pushed with fear-based threats of illness and disease, as well as judgment, rejection, and abandonment. The underlying idea is that your body is inherently weak and fragile, and it's your biggest vulnerability unless you do exactly as you are instructed by these concepts. Unfortunately, people who believe these threats end up with a "negative body image," thinking their body must be fixed before they can accept the life that body provides them.

The goal represented is to acquire a "positive body image."
However, when he or she trusts these businesses to be "all

**knowing," the consumer doesn't realize that many of these pos-
itive body-image concepts being pushed are based on *unrealistic delusions of grandeur.***

It's not that the goal can't be reached, but that for most people the body image
often requires insane forms of physical and psychological sacrifice that must
be sustained in order for the goal to be maintained. Consumers end up chasing a mirage, thinking that when the goal is reached, they can relax and finally
feel safe with, and accept their body. But as reality sets in, and the goal is
either unreachable or unmaintainable without suffering physically and emotionally. Instead of seeing the concept sold to them as flawed, consumers
blame themselves for being weak and incapable of handling what they were
told was "easy."

No one questions the persuasive ideal being encouraged. Without examining
the body-image concept being sold, total power over whether a person can
accept his or her body is given to businesses pushing ideas of health and inclusion that more often than not, are figments of the imagination. And I suspect these figments can be traced back to people who could arguably be
analyzed as sociopaths or malignant narcissists who seek authoritarian control and power over others.

Unfortunately, followers naively trust these concepts as if it's their life purpose
to achieve, and that the body shown to them is who they are. The body image
becomes their identity, and how they understand their worth to society. For
some people, instead of living their life open to learning, exploration, and
creativity, they get trapped by their devotion to a body image, thinking someday it will be "good enough."

As someone accepts and internalizes the body-image concept of thin(ner)
supremacy, it then becomes an unnoticeable personal belief. What is noticed,
however, is that a person who is fatter isn't viewed with as much value as the
thinner person who is automatically given a higher standing. You won't notice

that the thinner ideal is 1) why you feel bad about your body, 2) why you think people who are thinner are more attractive and valuable, or 3) why you also yearn to be thinner.

A person assumes excess weight is what she's battling, but what she doesn't see is the desire for the internalized ideal she judges her body by—*that is instigating this battle.*

When Weight Loss Looks Like Survival

Over years of closely monitoring people reinforce a medical weight-loss program that required strict food restrictions, what I found was that the more underlying body-image strain a person had, the more likely she was to have increased cognitive distortions, all-or-nothing thinking, and the more her behavior and thoughts about food mimicked people in poverty. Conversely, as clients who had less emotional needs for weight loss and less thin-supremacy beliefs, I observed that their emotional response to the exact same medical weight-loss program was significantly different. They didn't show the same sensitivity to deprivation, emotional strain, and cognitive distortions about the weight loss and the food restrictions before, during, and after the process.

This observation brought me to ponder the influence survival mechanisms have on:

- People who are attracted to extreme dieting as an emotional resolution for negative body image.

- How those survival mechanisms impact a participant's perceptions about food and eating restrictions while dieting.

- If those survival mechanisms predispose dieters to have cognitive distortions about the fat- and size-loss results when trying to reinforce a food restriction plan.

- If without those activated survival mechanisms, a person's response to the food restrictions and the physical results were different.

The reason a person is attracted to and holds herself so tightly to radical cult ideals, like thin(ner) supremacy *as a way to survive*, is incredibly complex, and for the person living it, it is very difficult to understand. There are unseen forces, unquestioned beliefs, and possible trauma supporting her drive to harm her life with inhumane dieting concepts, in order to survive. There are perceived threats that make starvation appear "healthy" and dieting look virtuous.

For this reason, people might be attracted to radical food restrictions as a way to seek protection from perceived threats to her survival needs in order to feel worthy of inclusion.

The innate drive for inclusion with family, friends, and community is a motivation that has been studied and theorized as a psychological survival need by world-renowned scientist, Dr. Abraham Maslow (1908–1970). According to his research studying human motivation and behavior, our drive to do whatever is necessary to feel secure with our family and in our community, is a required survival need.

Evolutionary Psychology, Survival Mode, and Maslow's Hierarchy of Survival Needs

Dr. Abraham Maslow's pivotal work described our fundamental psychological drives being based on securing the most important life-and-death needs. Dr. Maslow is best known for what is called the "hierarchy of needs." He maintained that before anything else, our mind and psychological drive is motivated to first secure and to make safe the most important fundamental needs that keep us alive. Once those needs are secure, then our mind can be relieved from the self-centered focus and nature of "survival mode" to now be opened to prioritize additional, but less-important survival needs.

Survival mode is hard-wired physiological, psychological, and behavioral mechanisms triggered by apparent insecurity to handle perceived, or actual dangerous threats. In terms of how survival mode functions psychologically, it directs your thoughts and focus inward, toward self-preservation.

- This mode of existence is emotionally and physically geared toward securing safety, removing risk, and responding to threat with forceful life-preserving and death-avoiding behavior.

- These involuntary mechanisms have evolved over tens of thousands of years—of running or hiding from predators, surviving and preparing for famine, and fighting threats to keep ourselves and our loved ones safe from harm or death.

- The sensitive response to apparent dangers, and preventative forecast of threat, has become so important to the survival of our species that this mode is activated even if the threat is simply suspected or perceived.

- Survival mode can be triggered even if you experience something as simple as the stress felt when facing a situation in life you feel challenged to handle.

- Danger doesn't have to actually exist.

According to *Oxford Living Dictionary,* a "threat" is a person or thing likely to cause damage or danger, or the possibility of trouble, danger, or ruin. The keywords here are "likely" and "possibility." Threat doesn't have to be guaranteed to create a biological response in the body. It only has to be a *perceived possibility,* which means any threat you think could happen can trigger a degree of survival mode.

It's as if the brain has a "danger probe" attached to it, like an invisible antenna that is geared to seek what you think you can't handle, and to detect vulnerability or potential danger.

This probe magnifies and surveys the environment, people, their body language, and any situation, animal, or bug that memory has recorded "as dangerous." Perceptions of threat promote the physical mechanisms necessary to react to that stress, whether it's to freeze in panic, hide in insecurity, run away (flight), or fight in self-defense. Even if there is no actual danger or risk, the feeling of insecurity can trigger this response. Our perceptions have a physical impact, and survival mode consequently impacts our perceptions.

> **NOTE:** When looking at mechanisms of survival mode, this response is directly promoted by the fundamentals of evolutionary human psychology. Evolutionary psychology is based around the notion that throughout past ages, as humans have evolved physically to survive the environment, we have also evolved psychologically. *The foundation of our psychological wiring is based on the need, drive, and desire to survive—to stay alive and to avoid death.* It would make sense that our minds are pre-wired to be attracted to and defensive of necessary life needs, like food, water, shelter, and a sense of inclusion in our community.

Based on Maslow's Hierarchy of Needs, you could say we have a psychological "danger probe" that is very sensitive to perceptions of danger that we perceive are threatening to the most important survival needs and not as much to the less-important survival needs. Maslow's pyramid gives a visual representation of what he theorized was the largest triggers to survival mode at the bottom (food, water, shelter, belonging) and freedom from survival mode as you move toward the top (exploration, spiritual endeavor, enlightenment, etc.). Then the goal of our survival mechanisms would be to secure these most important survival needs so that our "danger probe" can be turned off, in order to allow our mind to relax and experience the freedom to explore and enjoy our lives.

> **The idea is that by securing your most important survival needs, your mind opens, the way you function in life evolves, and you'll have confidence to explore and expand your experience in life, without feelings of inadequacy.**

I contend this is the mirage many people are chasing when they strive for a "positive body image," and what people who are devoted to thin(ner) supremacy envision in their mind when they fantasize about what a weight-loss program will provide them emotionally. They are seeking to fulfill Malsow's third hierarchy of survival needs.

Maslow's Third Hierarchy of Need: Love and Belonging

Maslow's third hierarchy of need encompasses the innate survival motivation to feel worthy of love and to be seen as a valuable member of one's community—and to have something to give, something to share, and something to add to the society. It also encompasses our instincts to avoid, deny, hide from, and prevent criticism, ridicule, embarrassment, guilt, and shame.

> **Maslow's third hierarchy of need is very important because when working functionally with others as a team to survive, the primary, more-important hierarchies of need, are more likely to be fulfilled.**

Evolutionary psychologists theorize that our inherent drive to belong in a group stems from tens of thousands of years with dramatic improvements to survivability and safety that occurred when people lived in small groups, helping and working together as a team. Ultimately, this evolved into a survival need, to the point that our motivation to "fit in," feel valued, and feel safe with others feels like a life-or-death matter.

Our brains have been wired to release pleasurable signals of safety when we have a purpose in the group, are accepted, needed, and loved. Conversely, our brains are also wired to experience withdrawal and negative irritating fight-or-flight signals when we perceive there is potential threats tied to being demoted or rejected. Those signals are more intense:

1) the more inadequate a person feels within herself, and
2) the more she needs her group to survive.

According to evolutionary psychology, our inborn drive to avoid rejection evolved in times of disease and scarcity to prioritize survival of the group over the survival of the individual. If there was food shortage or famine, the group would prioritize rations of food for those that contributed and were perceived as beneficial to the group. The sick and needy were stigmatized, given less food, and in dire situations, were abandoned to fend for themselves in the wilderness, which meant certain death. *Rejection, when survival is dependent on your tribe, equates to death.*

As an evolved danger, the perception of abandonment, or being worthy of abandonment, still triggers fight-or-flight mechanisms today, as if we continue to live in the wilderness and will die alone if we don't secure relationships with others.

If someone important to you is disappointed in you, you aren't going to die, but emotionally it can feel catastrophic. When there's apparent threat of disapproval, the brain has warning mechanisms that are like loud sirens, bright flashing lights, and magnified threat signals that get triggered when something dangerous seems to be happening. Immediately, involuntary self-preserving defense mechanisms get activated, which is similar to if you were encountering a dangerous predator. You feel the urge to fight, freeze in your tracks, or run away and hide.

In the case of social condemnation, your perceived mistakes and the group's disapproval are the predator. In effect, when a person is radically insecure within herself, the need to be secure with family, friends, or community can take over all other survival needs.

A person's perceptions of being important to a group increases confidence in his or her survivability—that there's security in advance of threat or danger. In addition, as roles and relationships in a group become more predictable and secure, the capacity to explore, mate, and to innovate expands. These benefits can give the impression that *the third hierarchy of need—to be included and belong*—is more important than the first and second hierarchy of needs. Although, as working with others brings increased capacity to survive, it also brings competition, shared resources, relationship and communication problems, and the risk for being judged and rejected.

You could say this need and motivation to belong is based on the fact that humans are similar to other pack animals, like dogs, that thrive when working together to support life. But this comes with the downside of being territorial, competitive, and with pecking orders when resources are insecure or scarce. Perceptions of not being valued by others feels as if you're at higher risk for uncontrollable death.

No different from dogs that act out when neglected and abused, we too function and survive better when we feel secure, can give and receive love, and experience a sense of purpose. For this reason, a great deal of psychological wiring that drives motivation is geared to preserve and defend ourselves from judgment, rejection, and abandonment.

"Fitting In" and Survival Mode

One of our hardwired survival instincts that is directly related to Maslow's third hierarchy of need, is the drive to "fit in" to our community and with our family. Evolutionary wise, this includes looking the part and blending into your culture. Our mind's survival "danger probe" seeks any information in our environment that might indicate safety or danger. One of the signals our survival mechanisms are probing for is *repetition*. Whether it's repeated danger or repeated safety, our mind is seeking to learn from consistency in order to predict what we'll experience in any given environment. *Repetition ultimately equates to safety.*

Humans are dominantly visual beings, and the ability to not stick out as visually different is considered a vital safety mechanism, particularly in environments that feel vulnerable to danger. Imagine traveling to a foreign country where their common dress code is dramatically different than what you are wearing. It would be instinctive to feel the urge to purchase new clothing that would allow you to blend into their culture, so you do not stick out as an obvious outsider.

The survival illusion is that the more you see repeated images, especially consistent pictures associated with safety, the more likely you are to feel the urge and desire to adapt to that image.

When you consider how you feel about your physique, your conclusions are probably based on comparing your body to images repeated and seen in public, with your friends and family, and commonly on TV and social media.

Our minds are wired to relax as we see repetition and consistency in how people look. Therefore, the more often you see images of the same type of body repeated over and over again, your mind unconsciously perceives the image as safe and "attractive." With that said, it makes sense why scientists who study the psychological impact of unrealistic body images, would suggest the media portray images that more realistically match our multicultural reality. Naturally, when a person wants to be accepted, she seeks to become what is positively admired by important people around her. To do this, she'd have to compare herself to the ideal of what she's being encouraged to be, and from there work to conform.

This type of *social comparison* is how people come to understand if they "fit in."

> **NOTE:** In 1954, Leon Festinger, a social psychologist, proposed that when a person can't find a fair or objective understanding of how she "fits in," she often compares herself to others in order to fulfill the basic human drive for self-evaluation.[4]

The more often people see repeated glamourized and promoted images of the body, the more likely they are to compare themselves to those images to assess their acceptability.[4]

The goal is to not stand out as different, especially if different equates to being seen as bad or inferior. Not fitting in would feel as if you aren't worthy of inclusion, aren't welcome or trustworthy, and might end up being an outcast.

When multiple generations have supported thin(ner) supremacy, and the people who are praised in the media and real life are all thin and look similar, evaluating oneself in contrast to those images to see how you compare would be understandable. The survival goal is to not be the obvious "outcast." As a result, it would be understandable for most "normal" or larger people to feel a sense of danger about their size and weight, more than ever when women who compare themselves to consistent images in the media that are considered 20 percent underweight.[5]

Today—when there's more body acceptance and diversity shown than in the past—more often than not, the images of people that are used in the media are air brushed and unnaturally distorted. For women, arms are thinned out. For men, arms are made more muscular. Necks and legs are extended, butts, boobs, and lips are magnified, waists are carved out to be thinner, and hair is made to look thicker, etc.

These repeated images are often paired with narcissistic sym-

**bolism, inferring they are the ultimate superior body types—
and having that body type will make you appear superior, too.**

For this reason, I assume the majority of people who repeatedly *see and
imagine* that these images are attainable will assume their body, in comparison, is inadequate. And the effort put into achieving these standards
will be far beyond what any human should be expected to do, just to feel
worthy of inclusion.

Based on narcissistic body images pushed by businesses making a financial profit
selling products, programs, and services that apparently help consumers "fits
in," it would make sense for why so many people who support these standards
fear their body and seek ways they can blend in, in order to pacify that fear.

How this applies to Maslow's third hierarchy of need, is that if a person's
body doesn't "fit in," it becomes a dangerous threat, taking away the opportunity for acceptance, inclusion, and is the reason for being left out and excluded. This is the basis for a "negative body image," and it would seem as if
fixing the body to match what is "good" and praised would help people feel
positive about themselves. When a person "battles her weight," she is in survival mode, battling a negative body image.

**This is what happens when you repeatedly see pictures of ide-
alized body images through the media and in your community.
Eventually the mind adapts to this repetition as a signal of
safety, and there are feelings of pleasure when you speak, act,
and dress like those around you.**

Being too different would feel bad.

If being different feels exposing, unsafe, and vulnerable to disapproval, it
would make sense to create an alternative identity based around predictable
concepts of acceptability. This is similar to animals that blend into their en-

vironment (camouflage) in order to not stick out. Humans are impelled to do the same thing, and *this isn't always a bad thing!*

It would be understandable that a person perceived as different or "unsafe" would want to change the way she looks, and try to imitate others so that she doesn't stand out, seem threatening, or draw negative attention to herself. Mechanisms that direct energy and focus toward securing one's safety, get harnessed toward memorizing, learning, and consuming as much information as possible to become what is predictably valued in society. The downside of this type of harnessed focus is that it ensures a person will know far more about cultural ideals than she does her innate and truthful human qualities.

In cultures that promote thin(ner) supremacy, where fatter bodies are labeled as inferior, inadequate, and are assumed worthless, it would be expected that believers who are larger and vulnerable to the "danger" of being excluded or not fitting in, would show emotional signs of activated survival mechanisms directly tied to a threatened third hierarchy of need. They would experience feelings of shame, and would be driven to behave in such a way that defends and protects them from dangers of abandonment and rejection.

Not only would they feel impelled to hide, but to also fix the body that is perceived to be the source of shame.

> **This is why many people are attracted to dieting, especially when advertisements and media used to sell weight-loss programs promote images that imply improved self-esteem, confidence, social inclusion. They are not just selling fat loss, but they are selling fat loss as a way to remove agitating survival mechanisms associated with shame.**

Survival Mode and Stigma

Every single person that comes to me for help fears her body. She's afraid of what the body is, what it could be, what it isn't, and how others perceive it.

To these clients, their body and the stigma of being overweight is their biggest threat and the biggest source of strain in their life.

As praised body images have gotten thinner, leaner, and more difficult to achieve, exercise and food-restricting concepts have become more radicalized. As a result, there's a rising trend in people seeking help and relief from disordered eating that looks similar to an eating disorder. As more and more people suffer from mental health problems resembling eating disorders, the social impact of stricter body images, stigma, and resulting extreme diets needs to be addressed, chiefly the impact that stigma has on the physiology of the body.

> **NOTE:** The term *stigma* dates back to the Greeks. They cut or burned marks into the skin of criminals, slaves, and traitors in order to identify them as tainted or immoral people who should be avoided.[6] Today, it is not a physical mark but instead an attribute that results in widespread social disapproval.
>
> Stigma has three fundamental components: 1) recognizing difference, 2) devaluation because of that difference, and 3) that it occurs in social interactions. Because of this, stigma does not reside in the person but rather in the social context, therefore, what is stigmatizing in one social context may not be stigmatizing in another situation.[6]

As it relates to obesity, weight bias and stigma assumes, when compared to the superior thinner ideal, the more fat a person has is a mark of disgrace, which defines his or her character and quality as a person as inferior. This translates to a survival risk of abandonment and exclusion.

> **Today, the view that someone has excess weight is the fourth prevalent source of discrimination, behind gender, race, and age, and unfortunately, stigmatization and bullying can start very early in a child's life.[7]**

The idea behind the stigma of body fat is that obesity is a choice—that people who are obese lack self-discipline, are lazy, and are inferior human beings. This ignorant attitude is deeply ingrained in public psyche, and the judgment towards obesity has affected millions of people, causing serious psychological consequences, and adverse effects to their physical health.

Shame About Your Body and the Stress Response

Like the natural fear we'd expect when standing in front of a hungry bear, in a thin(ner) supremacy culture, body fat is also experienced as a dangerous threat. It makes sense that scientific studies correlate stigma and shame to signs of stress to psychological and biological fight-or-flight mechanisms.[1, 19, 21]

> **NOTE:** As stigma and shunning elicits a sense of danger that you are at risk of being seen as having no social value, and that you are worthy of disapproval and being deserted to survive alone— the internal emotion of shame triggers the impulse to fend for individual survival needs in order to sustain life independent of others.[8]

> People living with chronic shame can experience paranoia, delusions, and psychosis, and are often cruel to themselves and others.[49] The thought is that if you believe you are worthy of shame, others are worthy of being shamed too.

Shame is linked to fighting for personal survival by seeking what will make oneself feel better, without having to rely on others. The idea is that when you don't feel safe with your own family, friends, and society, our instincts are to take care of our insecurities by becoming self-preserving and self-soothing. In effect, the idea is to protect your ability to survive alone. The value of pleasure that isn't reliant on others becomes more and more important. Drugs, alcohol, medication, but especially food, has been seen as a way to self-soothe, or to preserve one's own sense of survivability.[10]

Shame, and the loss of social status, enhances the value of Maslow's first and second hierarchies of need. According to scientists, the value of food goes up significantly as more shame is experienced.[8]

Food and other pleasurable stimulus mediate a temporary artificial sense of safety, security, and ease when your beliefs trigger inner survival mechanisms that tell you to fear others and yourself. To cope with abandonment, these outside pleasurable behaviors and substances provide an inner sense of safety and validation, without the risk of rejection. But, the side effect can damage your body, mind, and important relationships in your life.

Because the stigma and negativity attached to obesity is generally accepted, people who have more fat are more likely to experience social rejection, viewed as less desirable dating partners, have less friends, and spend less time with friends. This makes a person vulnerable to isolating herself, depression, anxiety, low self-esteem, poor body image, and in many cases, suicide.[25]

Often when a person feels hopeless about her weight, and she contemplates the overwhelming task needed to adequately restrict food and diet long enough, anxiety increases, and so does her eating behavior.

In a survey of 2,500 women, when asked how they cope with stigma about their weight, 79 percent reported that they turn to food as a coping mechanism, and that eating is a common way they deal with loneliness and stress.[11, 12]

Another study done with over 1,000 women from a non-profit weight-loss support group found that women who believed the negative characterizations of weight stigma, they blamed themselves, binge ate more frequently, and experienced higher depression and anxiety.[13, 14]

Compared to people who don't consider themselves overweight, when exposed to a weight-stigmatizing stimulus, such as fitness magazines or other media, those who perceived themselves overweight ate more immediately after looking at the media.[15, 16]

How a person relates to food is directly influenced by the degree that a person blames herself and maintains the stigma coming from important people in her life.

The more stigma a person experiences, and the more she upholds it within herself, the more likely she is to develop a binge-eating disorder.

Adults with obesity reporting weight stigmatization were three times more likely to have a binge-eating disorder diagnosis compared to people who haven't experienced weight stigma.[9, 17] For many, shame about their body is first experienced in childhood, which can alter their relationship with food for years to come.

According to a study of close to 400 teenage youth:

- After experiencing judgment and bullying about their weight, they coped by avoiding physical activity, increasing food consumption, and binge eating.[18]

- Teenagers who experience weight-based victimization have an 80 percent greater likelihood of severe binge eating, and the earlier a person experiences teasing about his or her weight, the more regular binge eating will be.[18]

- The more a child is teased, the more variety of ways that she is teased, and the more upset she gets about it, increases her likelihood of binge eating.[18]

Besides the increased likelihood of bingeing, in my opinion some of the most relevant research regarding body image is how internalized and experienced the stigma about being overweight influences the body's physiological "fight" response. The psychological stress experienced in regard to how weight is perceived negatively by others, has consistently shown to increase the physiological stress response described as "fight-or-flight." In other words, *shame about your weight puts your mind and body in survival mode.*[1, 19, 21]

Today we know that stress associated with stigma and shame regarding one's weight increases C-reactive protein levels, blood pressure, cortisol levels, and oxidative stress.[1, 19] Among other things, this stress response increases the susceptibility to fat gain, even when food isn't eaten to excess.

As well, media exposure to weight stigma, for people who agreed with it about themselves, showed a significant increase in cortisol reactivity.[20, 21] This means that a person who is ashamed of her weight and will think she is "bad" because of it, experiences signals of threat when she sees derogatory media about overweight people. The brain is responding to another's judgment and shame about her body fat as if there's an angry predator around every corner, stimulating the fight-or-flight response. The fat on her body is perceived as if it's a shameful life-threatening enemy. In this case, she lives in chronic fear, anxiety, and survival mode because of how her weight is perceived negatively.

Imagine the effect that this type of stress that's experienced daily has on a person's body over a long period of time, from childhood into adulthood. This alone would make anybody susceptible to hair loss, thyroid ailments, autoimmune disorders, heart attacks, diabetes, and weight gain—even if she isn't overeating. This is expressly true when you add the fact that people who experience stigma avoid the embarrassment of being made fun by avoiding physical activity.

NOTE: This embarrassment and fear of being made fun of has shown reduced motivation to exercise in both children and adults, ultimately promoting elevated blood pressure and increased physiological stress.[22, 23] Among adults with obesity, when they experience greater weight bias in weight-loss treatment, they are more likely to eat more, lose less weight, refuse that their weight be monitored, and expend less energy through physical activity.[24]

Research done over the course of the last decade, correlating the stigma of obesity and internalization of that stigma—to the susceptibility of weight gain, stress, anxiety, isolation, reduced motivation to exercise, depression, stress eating, binge eating, psychological and physiological stress factors—is overwhelming strong.

Combine that with the significant increase in binge-eating behavior—*no matter what starting weight, age, BMI, race/ethnicity, or socioeconomic factor*—for anyone who experiences and internalizes weight stigma, they are going to end up with obesity.[1, 2, 3] As repeated in chapter 1:

> **In other words, for those who support it, *weight stigma increases their personal likelihood of becoming and remaining obese. The belief in the "badness' of obesity alone increases your risks.***

Weight Stigma at Work and With the Medical Community

When people are in a vulnerable position to discuss their body, and are looking up to medical professionals for help, being treated as if they are inferior, and aren't worthy of care, can be particularly detrimental. It compounds the sense of hopelessness, judgment, and prejudice they already experience socially.

In a study of 2,449 obese and overweight women, 72 percent experienced a source of bias against them because of their weight.

- According to the National Education Association more people experience bullying in the workplace for their weight than for sexual orientation, disability, sexual harassment, race, or religion. (2011)

- To make matters worse, 69 percent of the women experienced bias from medical professionals.[11]

- Also, levels of implied weight bias among dietitians are higher than the general population at 52 percent.

- Among dietitians and dietetic students, most expressed anger and frustration with patients, assumed patients lack commitment, motivation, and compliance with health behavior changes.

- Of dietitians polled, 76 percent expressed moderate-to-high levels of unspoken weight bias. They might not say it, but they secretly think negatively about people with more body fat.[26, 27]

- A 2012 study disclosed that attitudes of medical professionals toward obese patients showed that they viewed these patients as lazy, lacking self-control, weak, sloppy, unsuccessful, dishonest, and non-compliant.[28, 29]

- As a patient's Body Mass Index (BMI) increases, physicians report having less patience, less desire to help, felt that seeing obese patients is a waste of their time, and having less respect for patients.[29, 30]

- It is not uncommon for obesity to be the topic of jokes in medical schools. Of 4,732 first-year medical students from 49 different medical schools, the majority of students expressed open and private feelings of very strong anti-fat weight bias.[31]

How Weight Stigma Impacts Willingness to Get Medical Help

When patients visit medical providers, they can sense discrimination and stigma. Parents of obese children often express feelings of being blamed by doctors, and so do adult patients. They feel berated, disrespected, and upset by many of the derogatory comments made about their weight.

Providers spent less time in appointments with obese patients and had less discussion with less intervention.[32, 33] As a result, patients are less likely to get preventive services, exams, cancer screens, pelvic exams, mammograms, and are more likely to delay, prevent, or cancel appointments and services.[34, 35, 26, 37]

In a study of over 1,060 adults, when asked: if your doctor would refer to your weight in a stigmatized negative way—almost half of the people said they'd feel upset, embarrassed, and would feel bad about themselves.[36] As a consequence, patients are more likely to avoid future health care, which in the end, increases the likelihood that medical problems won't getting attended to.

The Dangerous Survival Mechanism of Body Image

Whether it's to hide, run away, freeze, or fight, our minds are wired to respond when we perceive the possibility of danger or threat. When it comes to the danger of judgment, exclusion, and rejection, the urge to blend in and be seen positively in order to "fit in" is clearly a survival tool that benefits us and other animals greatly. However, what if that survival mode is triggered by concepts of body images that aren't humanely possible or realistic to achieve without suffering with symptoms of mental illness?

The drive to survive through a sense of belonging, is positioned to feel threatened by natural conditions of the body. Making your body a dangerous threat.

In terms of narcissistic thin(ner)-supremacy body images, for a person who upholds it, she is driven to diet and enlist in weight-loss programs thinking she is protecting her survival and will someday feel safe with herself.

But the truth is, they live in complete fear and anxiety about food and their body. This seems ridiculous when you consider that the body is responsible for sustaining life, and so is food. The problem is that what is triggering this response isn't a real threat—*it's a perceived threat for people who believe it.* You have choices when it comes to concepts of body image. What you choose can change, and in the case of thin(ner) supremacy, it should.

Request for my help from a woman in her 50s:
Hi Robin: I have been struggling with bingeing and dieting cycles all my life. I am 53 and started bingeing around 14. Your videos are so helpful, but I still have a lot of questions. I have just recently lost weight but abruptly quit my diet. I am in limbo trying to follow your guidelines to "eat to hunger." I'm afraid to weigh myself because I know it will throw me into a downward cycle, and I don't want to start bingeing again. I can feel the panic about to hit.

Readers: What part of her experience resonates with you?

1. Have you been cycling between dieting/bing ing/dieting most of your life?
2. Have you been trying to "eat to hunger," but are worried about your weight?

3. You're afraid to weigh yourself in fear it might
cause a ripple effect of bingeing.
4. Are you feeling panicked about your weight?

"The primary cause of unhappiness is never the situation, but your thoughts about it."

– Eckhart Tolle, spiritual teacher and author

Chapter 3

The Weight-Loss Mirage

"Ideal beauty is ideal because it does not exist: the action lies in the gap between desire and gratification. Women are not perfect beauties without distance. That space, in the consumer culture, is a lucrative one."

– Naomi Wolf, 1991 author of *The Beauty Myth*

The Weight-Loss and "Health" Fantasy

Most people who are battling their weight, are actually in survival mode, battling fear and shame about being seen as inferior because of their body fat. This shame has made being called "fat" a put down, as if being seen as overweight means you are the "village idiot." Over the course of the last century, this attitude has shaped a multibillion-dollar diet and weight-loss industry that takes advantage of our survival wiring as we seek to avoid judgment, by selling methods of fat loss with a mirage of safety and inclusion.

> **For almost a century this industry has advertised their methods as a weapon, shield, or "the rescuer" in your battle with weight, with the idea that fat is easy to remove and has the highest of rewards.**

Weight-loss marketing assures you that with their fat-burning program, you will easily reach the standards necessary to be accepted in order to get the life you've been aspiring for. The goal they are describing is relief and freedom from:

- Agitation and negativity attached to your body.

- Survival-oriented urges to shrink yourself and hide.

- Self-centered thoughts and preoccupation directed toward evaluating yourself and your body.

- Worry and anxiety about what others might think of you.

It's assumed that if you can't lose weight or be thinner, you'll forever be viewed negatively and at risk of rejection. You'll have to minimize your dreams as your body holds you back, and your life is less than it could be. From this agitated state of mind, anybody would be inspired to remove the blocks she thinks keep her from confidently living in the open.

NOTE: For some people the effect of pills, alcohol, or drugs can be used to temporarily remove survival agitation that seems to repress freedom in life. For others, it's the effect they get from shopping, gambling, being smarter, sex, fitness, having nicer clothes, a better job, a fancier car, a bigger home, another girl or boyfriend, going online to find a sense of community, finding acceptance in a religious group, or comradery in a sports team or political group. For people who support and sustain body images of thin(ner) supremacy, that freedom is earned when they lose more body fat.

Ask yourself: How do you earn a sense of freedom and confidence?

Freedom from negative perceptions that are coming directly from insecure survival mechanisms would feel liberating, if not "spiritual" or euphoric, as it gives the impression that you'll be granted the safety to move forward into an easier, open-minded space of independence. This is the "weight-loss mirage," and every weight-loss advertisement supporting thin(ner)-supremacy body images uses it.

It's clearly implied, as the before-and-after pictures show the difference between being seen as "bad," and then the transformation into being seen as "good." Every program comes with the promise that they are your ticket to living the way you imagine life could be lived—without having to worry or fear embarrassment about your body ever again.

Weight-loss advertisements over-emphasize:

- The confidence you'll achieve.

- How your life will change so drastically after you lose the "bad" weight that you'll be motivated to prevent fat gain forever.

- When you're thin enough, you'll have won the war against your body fat—proving you're a valuable person to society.

- You'll be put on a pedestal where people will see that you conquered the badness of your body.

- Others will admire your work ethic, dedication, and the newfound higher status in your community that fat loss has earned you.

- This will give you the confidence you used to have, or saw others had, and always wanted.

- Because of this you'll be willing to put yourself out there to be included, loved, and given the credit as the good person you've always felt you were on the inside.

This is the mirage people are chasing when societal dogma is trusted without question as a rightful way to secure a sense of worth and standing with their family, friends, culture, and society. They profit financially by portraying themselves as an authority, knowing what you need to do and how to do it, in order to fulfill your third hierarchy of need to belong. Through their program, you'll achieve the body they say is necessary in order to "fit in."

The dogma of thin(ner) supremacy is huge business, notably for people on social media that are profiting from promoting pride, glamour, and vanity attached to fantasy body images. The radical extremes of thinness, fitness, and ultra-leanness are seen hundreds of times every day, and are consistently advertised on TV, in magazines, and through on-line marketing. When you agree with these messages and seek to comply, this is why you spend the effort and money you do, over and over again in chasing the weight-loss mirage.

When dieting to lose weight has a 95 percent failure rate, clearly the claims that are made aren't achievable for most. Yet, believers continuously buy into it. However, discerning these beliefs as unrealistic isn't that easy, specifically when thinner ideals are paired with the idea that reaching them makes your body healthier too. This is explained in more detail in Section 2 of *Thin Supremacy*.

When Expectations are Unrealistic

There were times at the medical clinic I worked at, when we turned people away from the weight-loss program. A number of them came to the clinic thinking the program—meant for people with physical strain due to excessive amounts of body fat—would be an appropriate means to lose five to ten extra "stubborn" pounds, and were hoping to get down to a pair of size zero jeans.

When a person goes to a weight-loss clinic professing to have a problem, the people working there don't question the perception of the person seeking their services, even though he or she clearly doesn't have enough body fat to merit the need for intervention. Nowadays, if you aren't ultra-athlete lean, you're considered overweight by cultural standards, and a weight-loss clinic isn't necessarily going to argue when they too advertise you can achieve the same level of leanness with their program. In fact, the point of weight-loss marketing is to convince people to trust that with their program the ultimate lean size is achievable.

The more emotional a person is about wanting to be thinner, the more likely he or she will be attracted to programs that use images that appeal to their emotional insecurities, wants, and needs.

EXAMPLE: A 40-year old woman came into the clinic desperate for help. Perfectly dressed in her business attire, heels, and with perfectly manicured makeup and hair, she pointed to her hipbone. She acknowledged it didn't seem like a problem to anybody else, but that to her it was a REAL problem. Her clothes felt tight and she wanted to get rid of the pocket of fat on her hip because it was a terrible for her health. "I know for other people this isn't a problem, but I know my body and I usually don't have this problem. Plus, my knees have been hurting and I think by losing five to ten pounds my hormones won't be so out of sorts, and my knees will feel better."

She confidently explained how healthy her diet was and how her weight was easily maintained with her sugar-free, grain-free, nut-free, dairy-free, preservative-free, GMO-free, super-controlled diet. However, because her knees started hurting during her high intensity weight-training classes, she couldn't exercise, and since then has felt out of control, allowing herself to drink more wine and have some sugar.

This client described how she had gained 7.38 pounds, convinced the sugar was causing her weight gain and making her knee pain worse. "I can tell this added weight is making it harder on my knees. It's just not healthy, and I can tell the sugar is making my hormones go crazy." She was hoping the medical treatment (that's intended for people who are considered obese) would help her get under her 112-pound goal and get her sugar cravings under control.

When we questioned her dieting history, she opened up about her childhood weight problem. She talked about how she perceived her parents to be very unhealthy, and how she was embarrassed to have friends over. When she left home for college, she decided to better herself and to lose weight. Since then she's been able to maintain her thinness with strict focus, dedication, and control. She was convinced she was addicted to sugar and thought her food restrictions were the best thing for her health and weight.

She discovered the medical treatment after someone in an on-line diet forum mentioned she might have hormone issues that the medical treatment might fix.

She was convinced she had hormonal problems caused by the sugar, and thought she was a good candidate for our program. Recognizing her clear and obvious distorted perceptions, we gently turned her away.

Someone like this 40-year old woman wouldn't be attracted to just any type of restriction. Her needs were so intense that she actually counted her weight gain by the .38 of a pound measurement. Any time a client described their losses and gains by the .01 value, it is a clear indication of how survival oriented the drive to be thinner is, and how valuable the weight adjustments are, in gain and loss.

Considering her normal way of eating requires such extreme restriction already, it wouldn't make sense that she'd be attracted to a moderate approach to dieting. The radical restrictions of the medical treatment were a good fit for both her already-existing restriction, and her desperate need to lose the extra 7 (and .38) extra pounds. Her needs for thinness were extreme, and so were her feelings about being fat. It is that type of intensity that attracts people to food restrictions that have extreme and often inhumane demands.

We had many men and women inquire about our program that wouldn't normally be attracted to something as radical as medical weight loss, but they were hoping to lose weight rapidly for an important event like a wedding, vacation, or to meet physical requirements for an evaluation by the military. The more a person needs to lose weight "NOW," the more attracted she (or he) would be to more extreme weight-loss methods, particularly if her exposure to it *is from advertising.*

When the diets promoted in the media commonly use ultra-lean body images in their advertisements, and also claim that the best highest possible amount of fat loss is feasible, people with unrealistic expectations and more severe emotional issues with body image are more likely to believe it and seek it out. The images gratify the best-case scenario for their urges to control food in order to fulfill the survival desires to be thinner.

However, the body that's typically portrayed is a lie. The ultra-lean people featured clearly didn't have large amounts of fat in the first place.

The emphasized body image portrayed in most weight-loss advertisements doesn't show the excess skin or stretchmarks that would be left over after losing large amounts of body fat.

Thousands of times over the course of twenty years, I've monitored, measured, and caliper-tested hundreds of people gaining and losing body fat. Anyone who has had this much experience measuring people of all sizes would agree: there are physical signs of fat loss to be expected that look nothing like the pictures portrayed in weight-loss advertisements. A body that originally was appropriate to sustain a restrictive diet or medical weight-loss treatment in order to lose the amount of fat they claim, started in a larger body, with extra skin that only surgery could remove.

Weight-loss programs repeatedly sell body-image fantasies that make it appear as if their program is realistic for everyone, no matter what's your size. Whether you think having an extra five pounds too much or if you have over 100 pounds of extra body fat, the claims make it seem as if you, too, will look like the body that's depicted in their advertisements—which is completely misleading.

Consequently, dieters assume that if the advertisements claims are true, the sacrifice it takes to restrict food would be worth it. They are using the value of unrealistic and incorrect rewards to determine the cost and effort. The truth is, the best-case scenario presented, losing as much fat as possible in the shortest amount of time, would require that most people live in isolation from life, or live life in a "vacuum," completely removed from the vulnerability and temptations of reality. The risk is your sanity.

People derive their perceived ability and willingness to adhere to a diet based on an outcome that is far from reality. Without knowing it, dieters are set up ahead of time to struggle with the restrictions when they don't lose that much weight.

And even if the consumer doesn't trust the picture, they might believe the symbolisms and mirage that fat loss will free them from low self-esteem and shame.

Too many people jump into a weight-loss program assuming that the emotional gratification of fat loss is all he or she needs in order to be content with the strain and angst that goes into food restriction. *Unfortunately, this is the farthest thing from the truth.*

Let's Get Brutally Honest

As generation after generation of the vast majority of all people trying to achieve a more "superior" thinner body are gaining more and more weight, why haven't we recognized that this is an indication that the goal, and the means to achieve that goal, might be the problem?

Instead of looking at unrealistic body images pushed as "easy" to reach, we are directed to blame food, blame people's lack of willpower, and to blame their faulty body. Without recognizing that constant widespread difficulty reaching the goal and adhering to a diet plan is an indication the system isn't humanely realistic, it's understandable why the narcissistic dogma of thin(ner) supremacy has continued without question.

If the images being promoted as "normal" were required to reveal the likely achievability for the average individual, people could better understand how unnatural and inappropriate most body-image and "health" concepts are.

With that knowledge:

- Consumers would know the truth about the unrelenting focus, effort, and permanent food restriction it would require to reach and sustain unrealistically high expectations.

- The idealistic body-image standards would lose their "superior" status and appeal.

- Consumers would quickly identify businesses trying to profit by selling such rubbish.

- People wouldn't so quickly judge themselves or others who struggle to achieve unrealistic expectations and standards.

No one questions the validity and integrity of images that are promoted and sold as being easily reachable by an industry that profits from people feeling bad about their body. Without question, the weight-loss industry is given authority to define both what is the "right" body that provides a person with health, value, lovability, and worth, as well as the "right" way to restrict food to achieve this approval.

Like totalitarian control, no one looks at the body-image belief system that's dictating *what the look is that you must achieve* to be "healthy" as being dishonest and narcissistic—especially when it's inferred that ultra-leanness will improve your lovability.

What if the expectation that anyone can reach these standards, even if they must perpetually starve themselves, is recognized as insane?

If the majority of followers generally suffer from low self-worth because of poor body image, and they end up with a dysfunctional relationship with food, isn't this a reflection of the belief system and its strictness more so than being about the individuals who reinforce it?

As dieters chase the mirage that being thinner will allow them the safety and security to open themselves up to experience the life they want, they end up with more and more perfectionism, and worse and worse eating issues. The dream of being safer, calmer, and more independent in a thinner body isn't what they fantasized it would be.

Unfortunately, I've never met someone who takes pride in her thinner body and thin(ner) supremacy who has this type of freedom.

The problem is that weight loss typically requires a form of food restriction, and evolutionary wise, dieting might trigger a threat response to the most basic and important primitive survival need: food.

Not only are you at risk for being abandoned and rejected if you're considered overweight, but you're led to assume the fat on your body is going to kill you because the food you eat is dangerous. In terms of insecurity and fear, followers are positioned to have multiple apparent threats triggering primitive survival mechanisms. Your belief in these claims, as though they are unquestionably true, results in fear, anxiety and concern, no matter what size you are.

Email requesting my help from a woman in her early 40's:
I spoke to you last year for an initial consult. I wasn't ready to work with you—and I was not ready to accept my body where it was either. I dieted again and lost 12 kgs (26 pounds) using the ******* Plan (in Australia), and I became a consultant for that company where I help others lose weight too.

But I binged my way back up to weighing 75 kgs (165 pounds). I never used to binge until I started dieting. I have tried to get back on the diet, but I end up bingeing within 4 or 5 days! I can't even follow the program that I am selling to other people. Not only do I feel like a hypocrite, but also feel like I want to die.

My husband constantly says, "Should you be eating that?" as he knows the flogging I give myself when I eat off plan. I'm meant to go on vacation in November, and I don't want to go. I find it hard that I will ever accept my body and give up dieting. I don't know what's wrong with me. All I know is I've dieted myself fat! I want to give up my weight-loss business (I have 20 clients) as I don't want to be a part if this so-called diet industry. I wish I could escape this prison.

> **Readers: What part of her experience resonates with you?**
>
> 1. Did you lose weight with a specific diet, and then represent and sell that diet?
> 2. Have you regained weight you lost on that specific diet?
> 3. Does your family watch what you eat?
> 4. Do you feel like your life is in a dieting- and weight-loss prison?

When Body Image Gets Cultish

The promotion of more radical body images and fear-based dieting has become popularized by "experts" on the internet who more often than not, might suffer from their own survival mechanisms being enflamed. It's not uncommon that leaders in "health" see illness through the eyes of stigma, as they uphold illness or "unhealth" as a choice that symbolizes your value as a human.

Studies of people suffering with disordered eating that looks like orthorexia (an unhealthy obsession of pure and "clean" eating), describe personifying concepts of healthy eating as being sign of righteous morality. As described by Dr. Steven Bratman, the doctor who coined the term:

> **"It (orthorexia) has an aspirational, idealistic, spiritual component which allows it to become deeply rooted in a person's identity. It is most often only a psychological problem in which food concerns become so dominant that other dimensions of life suffer neglect."** [50]

To me, when concepts of "health" get paired with the vanity of being seen as virtuous, this is a clear sign that survival mechanisms are inflamed. Specifically, it is a threat to a person's need for being seen as lovable through narcissistic "health" concepts of body image, but also a threat to the need to feel safe from "dangerous food" through hypervigilant restrictions. My assumption is that these people suffer from a combination of two major hierarchies of survival needs being triggered as unsafe at the same time together. For example, if you don't eat healthy, your life will be threatened, and so will your standing and worth in society.

People with this type of body-image belief system would be impelled to seek to control and "probe" their food environment with underlying fears of food-danger and death, but also with narcissistic fears of exposure and embarrassment that would occur if they were seen as unhealthy.

Their goal of being seen as valuable in their community is using heightened survival mechanisms that seek to feel safe with food as a prideful symbol of and supremacy.

Ultimately, both insecure mechanisms exponentially magnify feelings of danger to the point that believers suffer with obsessive paranoia and hatred of "bad" food, as a shameful symbol of immorality and unhealth.

EXAMPLE: For me, having high levels of fitness and leanness defined safety with my body, but also the vanity of my desires for inclusion. It was an extreme double-survival insecurity requiring that I perfect both in unison in order to feel secure. In the end, this felt like my survival was cannibalizing my life—or that what kept me alive was killing me.

This type of dual-survival codependency can project onto other body images, like bodybuilding, sexuality, beauty, or fitness. In terms of anorexia, this would be like gaining the pride of thin(ner) supremacy through the pride of starvation too. In other words, your needs to "fit in" are holding your needs for food hostage, *in pride*. To someone in this state of mind, eating would feel like death, and so would body fat. Sadly—without both—death is guaranteed.

Like a religious cult leader, experts in health and fitness who suffer this way, think they are guiding others to the mirage of safety and freedom, but in reality they are unconsciously spreading shame and judgments based on information that's been distorted and catastrophized in their mind through projections of radical fear. Devout followers end up praising and taking pride in their intense impulses to probe their environment for impurities and "badness," as if life's righteous purpose is to make sure through survival force, that the body is safe from its own dangerous fragility. And others that don't do the same are demeaned. *"They don't get it."*

Believers truly think they are doing what's right, but in the end, they might end up suffering with symptoms of mental illness— thinking they'll die a horrific death without their narcissistic body-image and survival dogma to protect them.

From my personal experience with this, it feels like your mind and intellect are held hostage, and you are forced to probe and intellectualize the complexity of food and your body to the point of obsession. I thought that the more information I could learn about metabolism, fitness, fat loss, and nutrition would remove the extreme fear I felt inside. I ended up getting a degree in exercise science, and became an "expert" at fat metabolism. This gave my survival mechanisms a direction to work, through the illusion that with knowledge, I could control vulnerability. I was driven to insulate myself from being exposed by gleaning as much knowledge as possible to detect danger more easily.

This is what anybody would do when their mind is distorted to fight for survival. It's no different than wanting to understand the environment that tigers, bears, and other predators inhabit or might be hiding in. People in this state of mind are doing exactly what survival would request of them. They think that a sense of safety will be accessed through the power of the intellect, which is a mirage.

This is very deceptive, as it requires that you sacrifice the freedom of your mind to remain in a shrinking cage of safety. You might be "healthy," but life is disabled by this state of mind.

The human mind is closed and dualistic in survival in order for energy to be harnessed toward forcing an end result. Forceful. In this state of mind, it's very difficult to see relativity and to comprehend the dynamic nature of life. Therefore, the use of the mind to survive is a losing battle.

Even as I use the same survival "probe" in an attempt to intellectualize and understand the elaborate suffering of conflicting survival mechanism, it's impossible to actually "know" what's really going on. In humility, I contend we as humans aren't capable. We're aren't cerebrally and intellectually as evolved or as smart as our inflated survival ego thinks we are.

Notably in situations where food restrictions that are exalted by health "experts" have the unintended consequence of triggering primal psychological survival mechanisms to defend food consumption at all cost.

Request for my help from a woman in her 30's:
I lost forty pounds with a strict ketogenic diet a couple of years ago, and I've struggled with binge eating ever since. After perfectly restricting and losing forty pounds (which was my goal), a ravenous

unearthly hunger came over me and I ate insatiably. The hunger was so bizarre and unnatural that I was waking in the night to eat. Summary since then: many failed attempts to redo the diet, a complete inability to stick to any plan whatsoever. I feel depressed and have huge regret and anger at myself. I'm humiliated because I come from a small-town environment where everyone saw me lose weight, and now I've gained it all back.

Readers: What part of her experience resonates with you?

1. Did you experience a large amount of weight loss with radical food limitations?
2. After restricting food for a long period of time, did you experience an insatiable appetite and hunger that didn't seem emotional?
3. Have you got up in the middle of the night with insatiable hunger after dieting for a long period of time?
4. Have you found it difficult, if not impossible, to restrict the same way again?
5. Have you judged and criticized yourself for not being able to restrict as intensely again?
6. Did others recognize and acknowledge your weight loss, and are you now embarrassed and feeling worse about yourself after regaining the weight?

SECTION 2

The War Between Feast and Famine

"How can a single human cell measuring 1/1000 of an inch across contain instructions within its DNA that would fill 1000 books with 600 pages each? The more we learn about the workings of the body, the more we realize just how vast is the intelligence at work within it, and how little we know. When the mind reconnects with that, it becomes a most wonderful tool. It then serves something greater than itself."

– Eckhart Tolle, *The Power of Now*

Primitive survival mechanisms that are geared to distort the way we think should be the center of any discussion when observing body image and thin(ner) supremacy—chiefly how these concepts distort the way people relate to their body and to food, further triggering primitive survival mechanism specific to feeding behavior.

It is my intent to present this extremely complex topic of survival in a way that helps you grasp how it relates emotional eating, disordered eating, and eating disorders. My hope is that you can see the forest for the trees and have more compassion for your own humanness, as well as the suffering of others struggling to survive.

Chapter 4

When Access to Food is Threatened

"Dieting is the most potent political sedative in women's history; a quiet mad population is a tractable one."

– Naomi Wolf

The Dieting Mirage

When being thinner comes with the mirage of inclusion, it makes sense that dieting would also be part of that mirage. What most people who don't diet know is that there isn't a day where a dieter's fight with the body doesn't include a fight with food. His or her battle isn't just about the negativity and stigma of body fat. It's about the constant angst, tension, stress, anxiety, guilt, and shame about eating food.

People who are in a survival-mode battle their weight are battling their needs and urges to eat too.

When fears of rejection and abandonment are connected to body fat, people are impelled to restrict and deprive food in self-defense. As a result, an even-more powerful survival mechanism is activated, which is driven to seek and accumulate food in order to stay alive. When these two evolved life needs intertwine to compete with each other—*that is what I think promotes emotional eating, disordered eating patterns, and potentially what could result in the person suffering with an eating disorders, like bulimia or binge-eating disorder.*

With fat loss, you might feel better about "fitting in," but your relationship with dieting and food gets more strained and intense as primitive mechanisms amplify your motivation to eat as an innate drive to stay alive.

For this reason, it's imperative that anyone planning to restrict food on a diet understand the degree his or her motivation is based on survival mechanisms driven by thin(ner)-supremacy body-image beliefs. This understanding is important no matter what type of diet or food restriction a person is planning to reinforce. It would be helpful for people to connect the dots between how much their emotional eating might stem from survival impulses for food that are triggered by shame they hold about their body. This helps them realize they aren't "crazy" or lacking discipline when they feel urges to eat to compensate for having restricted food in the past or in anticipation of a diet in the future. Awareness of how thin(ner)-supremacy ideology and food-depriving diets might clash to promote a war of survival mechanisms could help people foresee and prevent these issues from arising.

Request for help from a 32-year-old male:
At one point I weighed 230 pounds. I'm down to 175 pounds eating a ketogenic diet and implementing intermittent fasting; however, I've started having terrible issues with bingeing. These binge episodes have caused depression and just knock me down. I desperately want to stop bingeing and stop using food to snuff out negative feelings. And yet, just as I want this, I strongly don't want to give up food at the same time either, even though it's ruining my life. Can you help me?

Readers: What part of his experience resonates with you?

1. Did you start emotional eating or binge eating after a radically food-restrictive diet?
2. Do you blame yourself and experience shame or discouragement after bingeing?
3. Are the radical restrictions that require perfection contribute to feelings of apathetic failure when you don't restrict adequately?
4. Are the feelings of irreparable damage and failure because of imperfect dieting contributing to the decision to binge?
5. Are you convincing yourself you will restrict perfectly the next day, prior to bingeing?
6. Have you started relating to food as a coping mechanism for depression or sadness?

> 7. Is this tug of war between radical restriction and bingeing taking over your life?
> 8. If there weren't a diet or way to fix the damages done from a binge, would you still binge?

Based on the research and findings of Dr. Abraham Maslow, the human need for being included is vitally important and was incorporated in his hierarchy of survival needs. *However, it is third in priority behind environmental safety and physiological needs such as food and water.*

Maslow's First Hierarchy of Needs: Physiological Requirements

The fundamental and most sensitive needs of survival are the most important requirements necessary physiologically in order to support the life of the body: food, water, clean air, sleep, etc. If these needs are threatened, insecure, or are not met, not only will you show signs of psychological stress, but the physical stress eventually ends in death. What Maslow found is that our mind involuntarily prioritizes focus, and magnifies the desire for these requirements if they are perceived as threatened, *more than any other need.*

The mind pushes less-important needs into the background, and brings forward all attention, motivation, and harnessed energy towards adequately securing these most important physical needs—*to above all else, stay alive.*

For example, if your food supply quantity is perceived as not adequate to eat today, cannot be replenished, or if it is not safe to eat, the mind will devote all attention to and emphasize what needs to be done to secure it. It will magnify attention on what tools are necessary to find food for immediate and later needs, places to forage and hunt, and how to stockpile enough food so the mind can be released to prioritize other less-important needs.

EXAMPLE: The clients I've talked with who describe the urges to binge, commonly explain the impulse to binge as being overwhelming and that it takes over their mind and all of their thoughts. Only after they give in to the urge, and allow themselves to eat without restraint, does the incessant pressure and focus on eating go away.

It is obvious to me that people who struggle with emotional eating and binge eating might be experiencing symptoms of this hierarchy of need—not feeling secure. If food supply is being threatened, you could say the mind will obsess to some degree on what it takes to secure food to make it:

  –   Available now,

  –   Adequate in quantity to support immediate needs,

  –   Safe to eat,

  –   Replenishable and stockpiled, and

  –   Good to taste.

MASLOW'S HIERARCHY OF NEEDS

This is described in more detail in *Hierarchy of Food Needs*, by Registered Dietician, Elly Satter, MS, RD, LCSW, BCD. Satter detailed what needs must be met in order to secure this hierarchy of need. Until food is fully and completely secure, the mind will need to keep thoughts of food and eating at the front of the mind at all times. It's as if your food is being threatened, and the mind's eye must keep constant watch over it.[38] Your mind will fight for you to get food, and this is experienced through urges, thoughts, cravings, hunger pains, and fantasies about food.

> **When you consider that roughly 97 million people in the United States diet, are preparing to diet, are just getting off of a diet, and that even more people don't diet, but think they should, that's a lot of people who are potentially threatening their access to food.[39]**

This is one of the most important physiological and psychological needs, which makes sense for why people feel impelled to overeat the food they intend to restrict again and again before and after the next diet—and why people with eating disorders describe being obsessed with every aspect of food. To them it feels like the focus on food controls the safety of their life.

Request for my help from a woman in her 20's:
Hi Robin, I have been struggling with anorexia, bulimia, and Binge Eating Disorder for five years. I just found your YouTube videos, and now I can see clearly that the only way to recover is to stop dieting! I still restrict mainly sugar and carbs, and I recognize I'm not ready to give it up yet. I think the problem is that because of the years of restrictions I continue to binge. I am still not satisfied after eating, and I can't tell when to stop. I get so anxious that I'm going to gain weight. I struggle to recognize when to stop eating.

This is the thing what makes me feel crazy...I am able to feel my hunger, for sure. But I have cravings for carbs, so then I try to drink lots of water to avoid eating, and then I get too hungry, I end up eating carbs, and I eat way too much. Ugh.

I tell myself that I am not on a diet, and I'm trying to eat when I'm hungry like you suggest. But I have too many fears about carbs and am trying to keep them out of my diet because I don't want to gain weight. How do I eat to hunger when I constantly crave carbs? I need your help!

Readers: What part of her experience resonates with you?

1. Do you restrict sugar and carbs because you're afraid you can't control yourself when you eat them?
2. Do you find that this type of fear and anxiety makes it hard to recognize hunger, satiation, and fullness when you eat?
3. Have you noticed the more you fear these foods, the more you think about them, and the more you crave them?

It doesn't help when the weight-loss industry bombards consumers with constant propaganda that food is unsafe, toxic, causes cancer, diseases, and is "bad" for you. Headlines such as "5 Foods You Should Never Feed Your Children" or "Toxic Foods You Should Know About" promote fear that food is dangerous, again creating insecurity to the most sensitive foundation of psychological wellbeing. This could be why it is common for people that are not secure with food to rely heavily on nutritional messaging on food packaging, as an unconscious way to ease survival mechanisms that have been inflamed by their fear that food is unsafe to eat.[40]

Because of the vital requirement for our physiological needs, particularly food, our psychological mind is highly sensitive to perceptions that food might be going away, like in the case of famine or a food shortage.

Think of dieting as a superficially imposed artificial "famine." In essence, when a person diets, she is willfully attempting to create an equation that translates to food shortage, all while she has immediate access to overflowing abundance of food surrounding her. This is largely problematic because perceived famine, or being deprived of food, triggers psychologically hardwired survival impulses to gain access to food in order to defend her life from dying of starvation. These survival mechanisms drive the desire to "forage and hunt" for food in order to keep ourselves alive.

The strain that people anticipate when preparing to diet is agitation stemming directly from these hardwired survival needs that increase desires and urges to eat.

It's natural for food restrictions to trigger our psychological drive to eat food in preparation for and while feeling deprived. Those instincts to defend one's access to food are what dieters struggle to control and repress.

Therefore, the natural state of our wiring is to sabotage food restrictions that feel threatening, as an unconscious drive to survive. The more those needs are "attacked" by a diet, the more our primitive nature to secure our access to food is triggered.

For some people, restrictions are set in place because of allergic reactions to certain types of food. For others, it's for a temporary spiritual fast, or a medical procedure. But studies have shown that these reasons don't trigger the same urges to feast, perhaps because they are motivated by more profound heartfelt reasons, and they aren't seen as "bad" or threatening.[8] The problem arises when restrictions are perceived as a punishment, or unnecessary, especially when food is readily available.

Restricting food while food is abundant around you takes incredible effort as the mind creates an angst, stress, or a strain that is psychologically agitating to your desires to diet. It's as if your survival mind won't let you focus on any other things, except food. It's like a bear preparing for hibernation—until you surrender to those urges and feed the primal animal motivations to eat, you live in the tension between the increasing appetite for forbidden food and the decreasing desire to restrict that food.

Compared to the strain and effort it takes to repress your natural desire to eat when surrounded by the smell and sights of food, and others that are eating uninhibited around you, it's easier (if not euphoric) to get temporary emotional gratification by joining them—even if it results in fat gain or physical stress.

What is consciously experienced is:

- Incessant thoughts of food.
- Fantasies about the taste of forbidden food.
- A magnified awareness and thoughts of the "bad" food you're not supposed to eat.
- Increased sensitivity to the way food smells, and how food tastes.
- Mental fixation on when, what, and how much you've eaten and how much you'll get to eat later.
- Shame for being too weak to obey the authority that's been given to the diet.

This was perfectly demonstrated in a famous scientific study performed at the University of Minnesota between November 19, 1944 and December 20, 1945.

Questions to answer and think about:

- ✓ When you feel bad about your body, do you feel pressure to restrict food, even when you know you aren't prepared or ready to diet?
- ✓ Have you noticed that when you feel bad about your weight, your urges to overeat increase?
- ✓ When you feel bad about your weight, do you feel bad when you eat?
- ✓ While adhering to a food restriction, do you have to remove food from your home and avoid social events in order to keep your mind off food?
- ✓ When you are restricting food, do you find that you can't stop thinking about food, and are constantly thinking about when you get to eat next?
- ✓ When you are restricting, have you noticed that micro-managing, counting, charting, and controlling every detail of your food intake, as well as the timing of when you eat, seems to help combat strong urges to eat? Or does this increase the urges?
- ✓ If you aren't under strict controls with your diet, do you feel out of control with food?
- ✓ When you've reached your weight-loss goals, do you feel an intense break in the pressure between you and food, like the flood gates have opened, and do you start overeating with careless abandon?

Chapter 5

An Experiment with Starvation

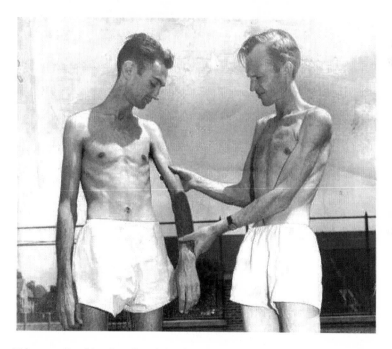

Volunteers Gerald Wilsnack and Marshall Sutton, c.1945. Image is from the Minneapolis Newspaper Collection, Hennepin County Library Special Collections.

"I just don't have the desire to do the things I should do or the things I want to do."

– Participant in the Minnesota Starvation Experiment

As I've monitored hundreds of people and thousands of attempts at dieting and food restrictions, I've come to also observe how that many people respond emotionally to radically restricting food. Over time, I've learned to prepare people for weight-loss programs in a way to minimize their perceptions of deprivation, as to minimize the risk of triggering survival urges to eat and prevent them from deviating from programs that have stricter food regulations. Even if participants were emotionally detached from the weight and size-loss results, and didn't show signs of hormonal starvation like hunger pains or energy loss that you'd expect from dieting, *I still observed symptoms that mimicked starvation in different ways.*

I observed that weight-loss program participant's taste and pleasure response to food was magnified in such a way that they described bland diet food as tasting delicious and euphoric. People described having a stronger sense of smell and having dreams of food.

Some of these symptoms undoubtedly resemble physical and psychological aspects of being starved of a variety of pleasures that's available when there's access to a diverse range of food.

I also observed certain psychological symptoms of starvation that would occur if a person is surrounded by food, specifically deprivation and perceptions of being punished or withheld from eating. These symptoms reminded me of the world-renowned Minnesota Starvation Experiment, done in 1944–1945 during World War II.

University of Minnesota Starvation Experiment

Thirty-sex men were selected and volunteered to undergo a 13-month starvation experiment where scientists studied the mental, physical, and social effects of food restriction, while being surrounded with food. This study was called the *Minnesota Starvation Experiment*. Initial findings were published in *Men and Hunger: A Psychological Manual for Relief Workers,* by Ancel Keys.

An Experiment with Starvation

Keys, one of the most important researchers in the field of nutrition, was inspired to understand and better respond to the physical and psychological suffering that occurred while people were starved in concentration camps. When World War II finally ended, one of his goals was to study how starvation, or semi-starvation, changes motivation, behavior, intellect, emotions, and social engagement.

The experiment's volunteers were to walk 22 miles each week, had daily work assignments, and were required to keep a diary. The only restrictions in their life was with food. They were free to continue to live their social lives as normal. Their food intake for three months started around 3,200 calories a day. Then they spent another six months eating about 1,600 calories a day, which was half the amount of food they ate during the first phase.

During the semi-starvation phase (1,600 calories), scientists observed an instant decline in energy and personal motivation, noting apathy, and irrational irritability. Many subjects developed strange eating habits, like handling food as if it was "precious gold." They observed eating rituals such as licking the plates, extending out mealtime, putting water in their food to dilute it and make it last longer, or even holding bites of food in their mouths for a longer time before swallowing. Food became a source of fantasy and motivation. Many men became obsessive about collecting recipes, and food became a central topic of daydreams, cravings, and desires. One participant journaled, *"Stayed up until 5:00 a.m. last night studying cookbooks. They are so absorbing I can't stay away from them."*

Men drank excessive amounts of water seeking to feel full, some took up smoking to reduce hunger pain, and others chewed gum, sometimes up to 30 pieces a day. They eventually banned gum from the experiment.

NOTE: I find this observation fascinating since I have worked with at least a dozen people who frequently binged on gum while restricting food. Many of these descriptions of over drinking water, diluting

food, and smoking to reduce hunger are also typical for people when
they chronically diet.

The researchers noticed dramatic changes in social motivation. They noted stagnation in the desire for personal development and relationships, and sexual desire significantly diminished. Social settings felt exhaustive, and pointless, and many participants didn't want to talk to other people. In general, the men preferred to be alone, went to movies by themselves, and even if they found something entertaining, they didn't have the energy to laugh or enjoy it. When out in public they were passive, slower, and were easy to push around.

> **NOTE:** *I clearly remember feeling this way when I suffered with anorexic tendencies. When I observe people restricting food on a weight-loss program, participants who feel emotionally strained with victim views of being punished or deprived of food, typically experience more agitation and anger in environments where they are surrounded by the sight and smells of food they can't eat. In general, this makes them less motivated to socialize, like going to the movies where eating popcorn and candy are obvious deviations from their diet.*

Sometimes the men in the starvation experiment would experience moments of inexplicable euphoria, but with intense emotional crashes.

> **NOTE:** *This sounds very similar to how I felt when I starved myself, and how others who suffer with anorexia also describe feeling—especially the euphoria attached to being able to control and withstand hunger pangs. You feel a sense of strength when you get past it.*
>
> *I've witnessed this euphoria with people who feel intense emotional relief with weight loss. These are the people that come to a weight-loss program with more intense goals based in thin(ner)-supremacy ideology.*

One individual was removed from the project because he was sneaking food that wasn't permitted when he'd go into town. He described a "high" he'd get eating food that was off-plan, and admitted he stopped at 17 soda shops one time on his way home. He reported being so happy and elated, and he felt the world was a beautiful place. But following his cheating, he was down-trodden and would have a period of pessimism and regret, and he felt like a failure for not being able to stay on the reduced rations.

> *NOTE: This reminds me of the excitement to binge, and the resulting shame many binge eaters feel, including myself, after not being able to follow a restrictive diet plan.*

> ***It's very exciting to know you're going to have a small window of opportunity to eat without feeling bad about it—until it's over, because then the remorse and self-deprecation is very intense.***

> *Again, this is more common with people who feel punished and deprived of food emotionally while reinforcing the diet they're doing. When perspective changes, these tendencies disappear.*

> *I assume this binge-eating euphoria and behavior is oriented as a self-preserving survival mechanism—like fighting and winning a competition in order to temporarily get access to food. But afterward, you feel bad because you did believe doing so is wrong or is an indication you are bad because you couldn't handle the deprivation.*

When the University's 20-week semi-starvation phase was over, the participants went through a food reintegration and rehabilitation phase. As they physically recovered, they continued to have lingering mental consequences. Plate licking continued, irritability became aggression when it came time to eat, and the participants' mood swings were more severe. It took three months for their mood and social behavior to even out and normalize. Surprisingly, the researchers found that the men needed as much as 4,000 calories a day to reduce the sensation of hunger during the reintegration phase.

The main scientist, Ancel Keys, convinced twelve of the participants to stay on at the lab for another eight weeks. He wanted to continue to monitor them during an "unrestricted rehabilitation" phase. Left to their own devices, Keys observed these men consume over an average of 5,000 calories a day. In some cases, some of them ate as many as 11,500 calories in a single day. One man was hospitalized for several days because he'd eaten so much; thus he needed his stomach pumped. For many months, the men reported having a desire to eat that they could not satisfy, no matter how much they ate.

> **NOTE:** *Based on my observations, people who are more survival oriented about weight loss and hold themselves more intensely to thin(ner)-supremist beliefs, experience more emotional stress with food restrictions, and feel punished and deprived of food. As a result, they usually have a more relieved response after a weight-loss program is over, impelling them to overeat. They often "lose control" once the restrictions are removed.*

However, the study found that the men's bodies returned to perfect health after a few months of consistent re-feeding. Some men in the experiment did gain back more weight than they had before. They gained back their original weight plus about 10 percent. But over the following six months their weight gradually declined as their satiation for food normalized, and they did not restrict again. By the end of the follow-up period, they were approaching their pre-experiment weight and fat levels.

The body can safely survive starvation and reintroduction to food. But the mind doesn't so quickly relax psychologically. The mind prepares for the possibility of another threat to one's access to food around the corner.

Email from 45-year-old woman who suffered from bulimia:
Hi Robin, I was wondering if you ever worked with clients who chewed and spit out "bad" food instead of puking it up? This might be helpful for some people to hear and talk about. I've suffered with eating disorders since I was a child, and chewing and spitting was so HUGE for me. For years my room was filled with bags of food to chew. It looked like a small convenience store.

I was 12 when it all started and finally today, at 45, I have my life back, thanks to you. I know I'm not a client, but I just wanted to say thank you for all you do to help. Attached is a picture of me taken 2 years ago when I was 120 pounds. I was so sick. Funny thing is that on the outside I might look like I'm happy and have it all together. Hell no! I was insane, miserable, and starving. I weigh 170 pounds today and am healing, thanks to finding your videos. My life is so much better.

I don't feel bad about those foods anymore, and I don't need to horde them. No more diets or fear of food! Thoughts come and go, but I know the way out of them because of your advice. It's so nice to live in a bigger body and not feel as if I want to die. I am so grateful to you.

Readers: What part of her experience resonates with you?

1. Have you ever chewed food and spit it out so you could taste the food without ingesting the calories or "badness?"
2. Have you lost a large amount of weight and other people thought you were healthy and happier, but in reality you were suffering psychologically with paranoia, obsessiveness, and depression?

> 3. Have you experienced the freedom and ease of not caring about your weight, and not having to obsess about food?

When There's Multiple "Starvation Experiments"

The Minnesota Starvation Experiment was instrumental in helping scientists get a better understanding of how the mind and body responds to forced famine. Still, for this research to be relevant to how dieting works, the participants would've had to intermittently do the starvation experiment multiple times, over and over again. Imagine how the participants would have responded if they knew they were going to have to do the experiment again and again and again, with a two-to-three month break in between.

- Would their eating have normalized the same way if they knew they were going to have to starve again in the near future?

- Would they have shown signs of emotional eating or binge eating prior to starting the next food restriction phase?

- What type of foods would they overeat prior to the next starvation period?

- What is the likelihood that they'd follow the restrictions the second, third, fourth, or fifth time they were starving themselves?

- Would binge-eating behavior increase as more and more starvation experiments are done?

In 2003, 18 survivors of the original 36 volunteers were interviewed as part of an oral history project about the experiment. They described that there had been some lingering aftereffects of the experiment. For many years, they were haunted by a fear that food might be taken away from them again. Imagine the impact on their psychological and physical wellbeing if the experiment was repeated over and over again, for years and years, *like chronic dieting does for tens of millions of people today.*

- As they fatigue, would they justify cheating on the experiment when they had emotional distress, social functions, or experienced increased hunger or cravings?

- What would happen if the starvation experiment included a competition of who lost more body fat, who became the thinnest, and who was deemed more "attractive" after losing weight?

- Would they feel bad about regaining weight during their rest period?

- With this "who's thinner" competition, how would the larger-sized participants respond when they are viewed as lazy, incompetent, not wanting it enough, or weak and lacking self-control?

- Would participants gain more and more weight with each rest period between each starvation experiment?

- Would their body ever go back to its prior original size and weight, after years of repeated under- and over-eating?

When you think about what the men experienced in their one-time starvation experiment, it seems harsh.

But when you look at multiple generations of people voluntarily submitting themselves to starvation diets, over and over and

over again—for the sake of trying to prove they are good and worthy people—the cruelty of it all is more obvious.

And the mental health issues in relation to food make complete sense. A person who chronically diets will predictably have stress and anxiety about her weight, as well as the reality that with weight gain comes another "starvation experiment." The truth of the matter is that people have been experimented on for decades, as "new and improved" diets have been released constantly for nearly a century.

For some people, the repeated attempt to restrict food has been with them for most of their life. It's not surprising to me when I work with people who've chronically been on and off diets that they have symptoms that look like a complex form of Post-Traumatic Stress Disorder (PTSD). This makes me wonder if binge eating is a symptom of "Diet PTSD."

Diet PTSD

Many clients I work with recurrently experience intense panic if they think food is going away. Despite the weight they gain by consistently overeating, it feels as if they are running away from food restrictions, or that they're running from a "diet predator." Part of the problem is that over time, they've developed a reliance on eating in order to cope when emotionally challenged, but they also overeat because it seems that they'll have to starve the rest of their life to lose the weight they've gained.

I believe impulses to overeat in anticipation of future food deprivation is a significant reason why binge eating, or emotional eating, is so common for people who chronically diet.

The stress a person has about her weight and health is minimized when eating becomes a more important need that shelters her from emotional stress, principally if she thinks the next diet will fix everything. And the longer she plans to restrict eating, the more intense her mind suggests she fight for access to food. She becomes "obsessed" as the urge to eat takes over her motivation and mind. Ultimately, the famine she eventually anticipates gets longer and stricter with each binge and with each pound of fat she gains.

> **NOTE:** *Like the double survival that occurs when a person suffering with anorexia has pride in both her thinness and also her ability to starve, a person who binge eats might have a similar double-survival need, but geared toward eating. As eating is used as a defense mechanism or as a way to survive life stress, there's simultaneously an increase in the urge to feast as body fat is gained. The more fat a person gains, the more he or she anticipates a longer and more intense "diet famine." The more shame people have about their fat, the more they are likely to binge.[11, 12, 13, 14] It's a cycle of eating to distract from life stress, then eating in preparation to lose weight that's been gained by eating to distract from life stress.*

The Minnesota Starvation Experiment provides a great example of how motivation and energy adapt when access to food is reduced. It also confirmed what Abraham Maslow had theorized in his pyramid describing our survival "Hierarchy of Needs." The mind will fixate on securing more important needs for life, such as food, until that need is secure both physically and psychologically.

> **It doesn't matter if you are starving because of true famine, a six-month scientific starvation experiment, or a 30-day cleanse, the body and mind evolved to respond to perceptions of deprivation in a way that preserves life—*no matter what.***

However, if you were to compare a person who is subject to a true famine where food isn't easily accessible—would they respond differently than a person who is food restricted, but surrounded by large amounts of accessible food?

Of course, feasting, stocking, and preserving food would be vital when preparing for famine. But if the famine is artificial, meaning it is contrived as food is in fact abundant and accessible, how would these urges impact a person's impulsivity to eat? This is an important question when preparing people for any form of food restriction. *How do you help keep people from not experiencing the impulses to feast before and after the artificial diet famine when access to food is abundant and perpetually available?*

After dieting and losing weight, have you been impelled to overeat and accept weight gain, thinking the next diet will help you 1) get back on track? Or 2) will help you re-lose the weight you're about to re-gain?

Ask yourself:

- ✓ When you think about having to diet in order to lose weight, do you feel a sense of angst or panic?
- ✓ When dieting, does your mind get hijacked by incessant thoughts about food?
- ✓ Would you willfully volunteer to restrict food if it didn't promote weight loss?
- ✓ Do you find it harder to stop yourself from eating after restricting food?
- ✓ Would you so comfortably overeat if weight gained were permanent?
- ✓ In your past, how much weight have you willfully gained, thinking a diet would correct things?

Chapter 6

The Battle Between Feast and Famine

"Fear, rage, and pain, and the pangs of hunger are all primitive experiences which human beings share with the lower animals. These experiences are properly classed as among the most powerful that determine the action of men and beasts. A knowledge of the conditions which attend these experiences, therefore is of general and fundamental importance in the interpretation of behavior."

– Dr. Walter B. Cannon, *Bodily Changes in Pain, Hunger, Fear, and Rage*

The Battle Between Wanting to Eat and Wanting to Lose Weight

Similar to a string of lights knotted into a mess that seems impossible to unravel, most people who come to me for help are trying to untangle the tight grip *between their relationship with food and their relationship with their body.* They've entangled themselves in a co-dependent relationship with suffocating diets to fix the dysfunctional relationship they have with food and the shame they have with their body. No matter how hard they've tried to loosen and relax the problems, they end up with more confusion, more tension, and more difficulty separating the grip between wanting to be thinner and wanting to eat.

When people come to me, they understand two things:

1. They have difficulty managing their desire for food.
2. Their food issues conflict with their desire for being and staying thinner.

People Seeking Help ...

- Don't understand why their desire for food is so high, despite the fact that they are desperate to be thinner and healthier.
- Can't stop thinking about food, what they can and cannot eat, and what they want to eat but shouldn't.
- Describe their fear of hunger, worry if they are going to get to eat, and constantly anticipate the next meal.
- Are burdened by anxiety about their body, what it looks like, what it weighs, how their clothes do or don't fit, their health, and what needs to be fixed.

Some people have been told they might be addicted to food, others identify with an eating disorder, such as binge eating. Some people come to me for help with emotional eating, thinking they need to learn self-restraint and increase willpower. Whatever the reason, they believe their relationship with food is the main problem, and they are seeking help to get control.

For most of my clients, almost every waking moment is held hostage by the suffocating pressure to eat right, to face the overwhelming task of managing every morsel of food that passes their lips, and trying to repress incessant thoughts about food. Food has the power to make or break their day, and the more they struggle with food, the more pressure they have to eat perfectly. *With help, they are hoping for mercy.*

Their hope is that I might somehow give them clarity on how to stop obsessing about food and minimize their emotional eating so they can peacefully restrict food to lose enough weight in order to feel better about themselves.

Adjusting the condition of their diet is the type of approach people have come to expect because the businesses and people they've gone to for guidance have always blamed food, and reinforced food fears and restrictions—with weight loss as motivation. When authority over dieting regulations is given to people and businesses who judge, fear, and shame body fat, it's easy to not recognize *that the dieting and weight-loss pressures they promote* are significant contributing factors to many people's overeating impulses and sensitivity to fat gain. This is very difficult to see when dieters struggle to differentiate their own psychological impulses to eat from true physical hunger.

Artificial Famine and the Impulse to Binge

Obviously, the discomfort many people experience when restricting food is increased hunger. But even without hunger, a huge amount of strain is connected to:

- Having to restrict while having food available everywhere.

- Wanting to eat to cope with stressful life circumstances.

- Agitation experienced when being around others who are eating food you're not allowed to eat.

- Cravings that occur due to reduced diversity in pleasure, taste, and quantity of food.

- Experiencing increased stress by restricting food while there's decreased weight-loss reward.

The strain that dieters experience is not necessarily due to hunger, but rather because of the complexity of circumstances they feel deprived in.

While there's easy access to large quantities of food, forecasted deprivation increases the likelihood you'll eat excessively, as an urge to "feast" in anticipation of "famine."

Restriction and Deprivation

Restriction is a limitation, or form of reduction. *Deprivation* is a negative state of mind that stems from perceptions of being withheld from what's available, like poverty surrounded by abundance. *Deprivation* is very different than *restriction*, because it puts a person in the position of thinking he or she is disadvantaged, or as a victim who could eat, but isn't allowed to—that everyone else gets to enjoy food, but not you.

NOTE: Eating on smaller plates is commonly recommended by the diet industry as a way to "trick" yourself into thinking you were eating more food. The idea is to reduce perceptions of deprivation. **But a recent study has found that when restricting food on a diet, people are more accurate at correctly identifying the proportions of pizza placed on larger and smaller trays than people who had eaten recently.**[42] To a person under the stress of food restrictions who is experiencing heightened awareness of food, a serving looks similar whether it fills a smaller plate or is surrounded by empty space on a larger one.

The author of this study, psychologist Noa Zitron-Emmanuel, said, "Over the last decade, restaurants and other food businesses have been using progressively smaller dishes to conform to perceptual bias that it will reduce food consumption. This study debunks that notion. When people are hungry, specifically when dieting, they are less likely to be fooled by the plate size, more likely to realize they are eating less and more prone to overeating later." [42]

You can imagine that when a person feels deprived when he or she is restricted, they are more likely to find a way to compensate for the perceived "unfairness" or entitlement.

Think of *deprivation* as a perception of disadvantage that triggers self- preserving defense mechanisms. It's a reaction to a perceived attack or offense where, in the case of eating, food appears to have been unfairly taken away. As a means of survival, you are positioned to fight for your right to eat.

If the availability of food is seen as disadvantaged, the mind's "danger probe" perceives access to food being threatened, triggering mechanisms that increase desire, more cravings, and more food-seeking behavior. In studies comparing dieters who are surrounded by forbidden food, compared to dieters removed from access to forbidden food, when prohibited food was available there was a significant increase in feelings of deprivation, cravings, and binge-eating behavior when food was reintroduced. [8]

According to research that investigated neuro adaptations to food scarcity as it concerns binge eating, Psychologist Dr. Kenneth Carr said:

> **"Weight-loss dieting amidst an abundance of supranormally rewarding foods and cues signaling their availability is likely to be stressful, and inevitably lead to episodes of loss of control."** [41]

He suggests that such episodes of food restriction while being surrounded by highly palatable foods could be hazardous as it contributes to binge pathology.[41] As an example, when you restrict a favorite food like pizza, when you see and smell the aroma of pizza as others around you eat it, you are going to feel deprived, resulting in a strong urge and impulse to *overeat* pizza.

> **NOTE:** These survival mechanisms to eat when access to food is threatened are wired into everyone's psych, no matter what size or shape a person is. Even if you're considered morbidly obese, this drive to survive doesn't just turn off because the diet industry says it's supposed to, or a doctor warns you you'll die if you don't lose weight.

> Evolved psychological mechanisms that took hundreds of thousands of years to develop don't simply disappear, just because we are surrounded by mass amounts of food, or because a person might have enough body fat stored to survive a natural disaster that disables his or her ability to get more food. The urges to eat will be there whether you weigh 100 pounds or 400 pounds.

> The more you anticipate dieting, the more intense your food restrictions, the more you feel deprived, the larger the impulses you'll have to eat, regardless of your size, shape, and health. In this

case, it would make sense that a person with more body fat to lose, who might have more shame, would have larger impulses to binge.

Undoubtably, trying to reinforce an artificial famine through dieting when food is abundant everywhere is very stressful to our primitive minds. When the motivation to restrict food clashes with hardwired primal survival mechanisms geared to gain access to food, it would seem sensible that anxiety would increase when dieters are around "forbidden" food. Unsurprisingly, evidence suggests reward for that stress can change how dieters respond. [8]

The Importance of Reward

Studies have shown that the reasons why you're restricted can make a direct impact on how people respond. If the reward for being restricted is seen as more heart-felt, like a spiritual fast, feelings of unfairness don't arise, resulting in less urges to overeat when food is reintroduced.[8] In comparison, dieting for weight-loss reasons showed impulses to overeat that were significantly stronger.[8]

This goes to show how overinflated the reward of the weight-loss mirage is. People think being thinner will be gratifying enough, but in the end the need for food is far more important to survival than "fitting in."

If reward and sacrifice appear equal, sensed deprivation and the idea that things are unfair goes away. In terms of the fragility of staying motivated to restrict food for thin(ner) supremacy body-image reasons, measured fat loss would be very important. On one hand, the more a person feels strain when she's restricting food, the more she'll feel urged to monitor, measure, and check her body for reward. On the other hand, stress and angst for dieting might not occur until *after* a dieter sees she's been deprived of anticipated weight loss. Either way, the urge to make things "even" will occur, resulting in food consumption.

When it comes to unrealistic fantasy weight-loss results pictured in the media and advertisements; the false expectations presented greatly contribute to why dieters who believe these pictures feel deprived of reward and will eventually end up overeating.

Even if there's sufficiently rewarded weight loss, the strain of food restrictions on survival needs can be intense enough that successful weight loss can be used as a reason to release oneself from the diet restraints in order to gain access to food without limitation. Weight loss is a bargaining tool to justify access to unrestrained eating. For some people, there is no amount of fat loss that makes up for the strain they feel being restricted from food, and the euphoric reward they experience when given the freedom to eat without the burden of shame and guilt.

"Addiction" to Food and Famine Relief

One way to describe the sensations that are experienced while in a mental state of angst trying to enforce "diet famine," while being surrounded by the sights and smells of "forbidden food," is "cravings." Cravings have been shown to be primarily psychologically driven, but that doesn't discount the physiological changes that occur when people are restricted and depleted of pleasurable food.

Your brain's dopamine response to food strengthens after palatable food has been restricted.[41] This means that the more you restrict a certain type of "forbidden" food, the brain is more sensitive to pleasure when that food is reintroduced.

This could be why the patients in the Minnesota Starvation Project thought the bland, flavorless food they were served during the semi-starvation phase was delicious. Their pallet was primed to respond more sensitively to flavor.

Additionally, as people hold in mind the food they crave, desire for that food increases, markedly when the food in mind has been restricted.[43] Even if you have access to an abundance of food, but restrict one certain type of food that you enjoy, it has been shown you will more than likely experience desire and cravings for that specific food, even if you aren't hungry.[43]

Studies suggest that when trying to restrict a certain food group or type of food, a paradox is created by an increased need to be aware of the "bad" food that has shown to increase a desired state for that food. When people try to restrict candy, they inadvertently think about candy more often than they would if they weren't restricting. In *The Psychology of Food Craving: Symposium on "Molecular mechanisms and psychology of food intake,"* obesity expert and professor of Sports and Exercise Science, Andrew Hills states,

> *"In the context of food and eating, there are circumstances in which trying to distract oneself from thinking about a particular desired food makes evidence of the existence and appeal of that food more prominent."* [43]

Add together the natural psychological magnification of foods that are perceived as "forbidden," the increases sensitivity of pleasure that occurs as it's been restricted, perceptions of deprivation that can occur when being surrounded by those foods—and it makes sense why a person would be set up to overeat. Gaining access to food you've been restricted and deprived of would be psychologically relieving. And overeating wouldn't be a surprise if it's anticipated that this particular food will be restrained again.

With both the agitation of feeling deprived and the physical sensitivity to pleasure, some people describe gaining temporary access to deprived food as euphoric.

When dieters think that as a lifestyle eating must perpetually be restrained, assuming the angst with eating must be "normal," it would make sense for why the positive relief that's experienced as euphoria would be used as a reward. The mind would seek any justifiable reason to get "famine relief" with the resulting reprieve as the goal.

To an emotional eater, this feels like incredible weight has been lifted off of your shoulders. For binge eaters, like a large rush of water when flood gates are opened, the moment temporary freedom to eat without shame and guilt is allowed, it feels like a large tidal wave of euphoria. *My guess is, the context of freedom to eat unrestrained without shame and guilt is what's addictive, not necessarily the pleasure of food alone.*

> **Ask yourself:** If you were to permanently get rid of restraint, restriction, as well as judgment and criticism of the food, would eating be as exciting? When most people answer this question, they initially feel excitement and think they'd overeat. But when they add the permanence that food will never again be restricted or deprived, that excitement dulls, and food becomes less "special."

Without looking at the psychological agitation that food restrictions and deprivation promote in the brain, it's easy to assume either 1) that food is addictive, or 2) that a person has an "addictive" condition. I suspect that prolonged and repeated dieting is the primer to what looks like a condition of food addiction.

> **What people are experiencing is an increasing euphoric survival response to eating that would be expected under any intermittent "famine" circumstances.**

The moment access to restrained food is allowed, resulting in physical and psychological relief felt as pleasure, people use this pleasure to distract from life circumstances that seem negative or out of a person's capacity to control. This would give the impression that eating improves emotional security when a person is challenged, when in fact eating is just relieving the truthful strain caused by a "diet famine" state of mind.

Because of this, dieters are put in a position to use life circumstances and emotions as a bargaining tool to justify, negotiate, and reason for why they deserve the grace and lenience to eat without feeling like a failure to their weight-loss goals.

> **Dieters are superimposing this "famine relief" onto life stress, as a shield protecting them from what feels out of his or her control. We call this "emotional eating."**

Emotional Eating and Bargaining for "Bad" Food

Diets and food restrictions are commonly taught with judgment and criticism about the food that's being restricted. Claims are made as if consuming any amount of these foods is "bad" for you, and if you choose to eat them anyway, you are choosing to hurt your body. This creates a moral judgment, as if eating those foods makes you a lesser human being. For many people, this judgment conjures up feelings of "doing something wrong" when they eat these foods. Unfortunately, this comes with negative feelings of guilt, as if the dieter has committed a crime or sinned by eating food the diet forbids.

As a way to reduce guilt and negative feelings in order eat and enjoy forbidden "bad food," a dieter must first justify why it's okay, and negotiate with the food restrictions for why he or she deserves the grace to indulge. The goal is to have the lenience to eat in situations where food restrictions are too straining and stressful to follow, but to also go back to dieting later as a form of penance, and to tackle the "battle with weight."

> **The underlying motivation is to create a sense of balance between the angst and agitation that occurs with famine and the irritation and shame that comes with the weight-gain after feasting.**

People assume their future diet will be a guaranteed way to remove the weight gain. Like teenagers who throw a raging party because they think they can get rid of the evidence and won't get caught. As a result, some people develop an emotional reliance on eating because life stress can be used as an effective bargaining point to gain access to "famine relief" without "dieter's guilt." This is one of the reasons why we have difficulty not eating, even when risks of illness and further physical stress with gaining more body fat is the obvious result.

> **NOTE:** When we believe with 100 percent assurance that a future diet will get rid of all gained weight, it's relieving to relax around the strain driving us to eat. Because of that relief, we are tolerant with overeating, turn a blind eye as our clothes get tighter, and are patient as fat grows back. Because we assume the weight gain will eventually get removed in the future, we live in a state of denial about the consequences of bingeing and we ignore the scale as weight increases. *When it's assumed that a diet guarantees that weight gained will be weight lost, fat you've gained as you overeat doesn't have to be acknowledged until later, when the "battle with weight" begins again.*

There is clearly a struggle in the strain trying to balance undereating and overeating, between dieting and emotional eating, assuming that with both there will eventually be balance, resulting in weight loss—and peace. In spite of this, with both the desire and pleasure of eating increases, and the body gets bigger and bigger. Ultimately, as the tug-of-war between dieting and eating intensifies, the battle with weight does too.

Codependency and Emotional Eating

For people who feel pressured to restrict food, eating becomes a natural way to cope with emotional issues, and also to gain temporary freedom from the strains and threats coming from "dieting famine." As a result, the more people diet, the more strain to eat they experience, the more life difficulty is used to bargain for the relief they get from gaining access to food, the more challenged people are to address their emotional response to life difficulty without seeking to eat as a coping mechanism.

> **Over time, it's easy to trust you're not capable of creating and handling emotions alone when life can feel challenging, as using food to cope has been unconsciously promoted by the current diet, and enabled by the next diet.**

As people go from dieting to emotional eating, then back to dieting, eventually a codependent need to eat in order to handle life stress can develop. Consequently, there's a weakening process that occurs to a person's sense of independence to handle life stress.

> **NOTE:** In short, codependency is an interrelationship between multiple people or things, in which the overreliance on the strength of one aspect in the relationship enables the weakness and neediness of the other aspects. Codependency is described as a triangulated relationship between a victim, a persecutor, and a rescuer. This is called the "Karpman's Drama Triangle." [48]

Typically, the victim needs a rescuer to save them from a person or situation that is viewed as the persecutor. The rescuer can be a person, drug, or controlling behavior that seems to protect and shield the weak and vulnerable victim. Unfortunately, the more a person needs a rescuer to protect them, the weaker that person gets in his or her ability to handle life themselves, and the more they grow an overreliance and need for their rescuer to defend against what seems like increasing threat. As one aspect of the relationship gets stronger and more controlling, the other aspect in the relationship gets weaker and less capable of functioning without needing to be controlled. *It's a cycle of excessive neediness between the two.* The stronger controlling side of the relationship relies heavily on the psychological reward of being needed and in control, and the other side relies heavily on being taken care of and rescued.

In the case of a diet, emotional eating, and the person battling her weight, the diet is seen as a rescuer when weight gain is the persecutor. When life stress is the threat, eating becomes the rescuer, resulting in the diet becoming the persecutor. Then again, as the person gains weight, the diet switches back to being the rescuer, and body fat being the persecutor.

Some people rely more heavily on dieting as their rescuer. This might be when anorexic tendencies begin. Other people more heavily rely on emotional eating as a rescuer, and they relate more on the side of a binge-eating disorder. Either way, there is a toxic triangulated relationship between the "battle with weight," dieting, and emotional eating.

In a codependent relationship with dieting and emotional eating, people lose touch with how to handle life, as they gain connection with the relief and benefits of either depriving food or emotional eating. In order to eat emotionally, they rely on a future diet to remedy the weight gain, creating a cycle between perceived life stress, diet-strain, then followed by eating and diet-relief.

Eventually, that diet relief gets associated with emotional relief, and because weight gain is viewed as the ultimate problem, dieting is obscured from being exposed as to why a person might have a more sensitive euphoric response to eating.

The relationship between eating and dieting and dieting and eating, is mutually beneficial, but not necessarily for the body. The result for the body is more and more fat gain, which ultimately increases the pressure to restrict food over and over again. Dieters end up chasing their tail, or living like a rat running on a wheel and going nowhere, thinking everything will be better if they could just be thinner.

When is Food Restriction Appropriate?

Look at how difficult it is for people to stick to food-restriction plans, not because they're physically deprived, but because they feel emotionally insecure or vulnerable in certain situations if they are not eating. Observe in your own self how often you've negotiated to eat for emotional reasons to end the angst you felt being deprived, and convinced that afterward you'll go back to restricting yourself to lose the weight you've gained.

The sensitivity to wanting food that occurs as a result of reinforcing an artificial famine while being surrounded by food in abundance is looked at as a personal problem. The food is blamed, or the dieter is convinced the natural euphoric response that occurs when eating after being deprived is an addiction. *But not all people who diet end up with these issues.*

As described earlier, the reasons why we restrict food and how much time we are removed from food, can change how our food-preserving survival mechanisms respond.[43] It's a matter of context for why you are restricting food. After assisting hundreds of people attempt a medical weight-loss treatment that temporarily requires very strict food restrictions, I have witnessed that the less a person is driven by fear and shame, the less likely she is to trigger survival mechanisms that impel her to overeat during and afterward. If she is open-minded about the results, and her curiosity to find the truth is her goal, I've seen many people diet without having problems.

> **When there is a more profound reason to temporarily reduce food intake as a choice, the risk of perceiving the restrictions as deprivation greatly reduce, and as a result the likelihood diminishes that a person will trigger mechanisms that drive the urge to eat in self-defense of her survival.** [43]

For example, the men who volunteered for the Minnesota Starvation Experiment did so as a way to improve the health care of people who were recovering from being held in concentration camps in Europe. Imagine having done the starvation experiment for a different reason—like as a way to prove your worth through the discipline required to handle food restrictions, and to repress the psychological strain that occurs when being deprived. You can imagine that in comparison eating behaviors and motivations would be different.

When preparing people who want to diet, I make them aware of the risks of feeling deprived, and the survival mechanisms that could get triggered while reinforcing food restrictions. If the intent of a weight-loss program is strictly physical as a medical therapy, the person is less likely to feel deprived and victimized by the temporary food restrictions—*as long as he or she isn't a victim of their circumstances or in fear of "unhealth."*

Alternatively, if their goals are based on survival through *the vanity of thin(ner) supremacy,* the likelihood that they'll finish the weight-loss program is less, and the chances they'll overeat when the diet is over, is extremely high. This basically guarantees any physical rehabilitation that might have occurred as a result of excess fat loss will be reversed, and the cycle of dieting and emotional eating will continue—particularly if the participants fear weight gain afterward, and that fear projects onto food as if food is a threat.

When motivation to restrict food is derived from survival mechanisms that seek to feel safe from judgment and rejection from one's community, chances are survival mechanisms that are driven to preserve access to food will get triggered.

The mind is fighting with the body, and the body is fighting with the mind. Ultimately, when two survival motivations are positioned to compete and fight with each other, there will be psychological and physical consequences.

Ask yourself:

- ✓ How would you eat at a party if you knew you'd have to permanently accept weight gain if you intentionally overeat?
- ✓ If there weren't New Year's resolutions to lose weight, would you still over-indulge during the holiday season?
- ✓ Would you change this thought process if you knew exercise and under-eating doesn't work to remove fat you gained by overeating?
- ✓ With that awareness, would you continue to allow food to beaten as a distraction and coping mechanism for emotional reasons?
- ✓ If diets didn't exist, would you have developed the same urges and needs to eat for emotional reasons?
- ✓ Have you ever wondered what you'd do if emotional eating wasn't an option to help you create feelings of security and to deal with hardship?

Chapter 7

The Mind of Survival Mode

"Our dependency makes slaves out of us, especially if this dependency is a dependency of our self-esteem. If you need encouragement, praise, pats on the back from everybody; then you make everybody your judge."

– Fritz Perls, founder of Gestalt therapy

The goal of the next two chapters is to better understand how fear and survival mechanisms impact how both our mind and our physical body works. This makes sense for why people would be attracted to believe in thin(ner)-supremacy body images as well why followers might end up with similar physical ailments and symptoms. Fair warning: this chapter might get boring.

When "Feeling Fat" Feels Like Terror

For me, gaining fat felt like getting murdered. I experienced an extreme terror, which is why I went to such drastic and abusive measures to defend myself by doing whatever necessary to maintain my leanness. Any other person with the same level of impending fear of being murdered attached to weight gain would do the same thing. I never would have thought my desire to be thinner was the problem.

When I talk with other people who have disordered eating, or eating disorders, they too have similar fear and with similar terror-like intensity. It doesn't start that way, which is why it's hard to identify.

> **You wouldn't suspect something as innocent as wanting to be thinner as being dangerous. *But when that desire is backed by primitive survival needs that make your body and food the enemy, it's not safe or innocent at all.***

Insecure survival needs distort and magnify anything it latches onto, making seemingly simple and ordinary ideas into radicalized notions. And as those notions become less and less flexible and more and more rigid, survival mechanisms gradually distort notions into zealotry and dogma. In terms of thin(ner) supremacy, fatter conditions of the body become a predatory threat to life, and the mind then responds accordingly.

> **When you "feel" fat you are actually feeling threat, as if you are easy prey to a predator.**

I recall this is what feeling "fat" felt like:

- It started with a dark, impending doom, and my body would involuntarily respond.

- I'd feel a flash of heat, my breathing felt compressed, and I'd start to sweat.

- My heart would beat so fast and hard it felt like it was going to come out of my chest.

- My hair would stand up on end.

- My stomach would hurt, and I'd feel nauseous, and it felt as if I was going to explode if something wasn't done immediately.

- My thoughts became erratic, like being short-circuited, and I couldn't think straight.

- It felt as if I was seeing through tunnel vision.

- My entire mind and body had an intense urgency to do something now.

- A horrible threat was there, and I needed to escape right now—as if there was extreme danger or emergency.

Each and every person I've worked with has described similar sensations. For some people, the feelings of impending doom or peril come when she feels deprived of food, and the only way to get rid of that horrible feeling is to eat. For others, threat is attached to gaining weight, which is why she micro-manages food and exercises obsessively. Like me, some people experience this impending doom with both food restriction and gaining weight, which is why they obsessively diet, and compulsively binge and then purge.

This has brought me to ponder the influence that both the fight-or-flight response and the controlling nature of sustained survival mode have on body image, disordered eating, and eating disorders.

Request for my help from a woman in her late 30's:
I need help after recovering from an eating disorder. I had a fear of being fat for many years throughout adolescence. I developed an eating disorder and lived with it for approximately five years. After going through therapy for two years I gained weight, but I am now almost forty and am still struggling. I have come so far, but have five children to raise, and I don't want to screw them up.

I am not as afraid because I have gained weight and eat more, but I am still very fearful of food. I have some digestive problems, and I believe eating healthy could heal these problems. But I recognize that I've become fixated on health like I was about my weight. I'm still obsessed about what I'm eating. I don't want this to control my mind any more, but I also want to be healthy. I'm worried my obsession with food will mess up my children's relationship with food too. I've heard you talk about health obsession on your YouTube channel, and it makes sense that I might now be Orthorexic. Is this something you can help me understand and resolve?

> **Readers: What part of her experience resonates with you?**
>
> 1. Are you an adult who has suffered from an eating disorder since you were a teenager?
> 2. Has your obsession with weight transferred to an obsession with health?
> 3. Have you defined health by the food you eat?
> 4. Do you feel bad about yourself when you eat "unhealthy" food?
> 5. Are you concerned that your obsession and fears about dangers in the food will negatively impact your children psychologically?
> 6. Have your children started to hide "bad" food from you?
> 7. Do your children binge on "bad" food when they are at their friend's house?

You and Your "Danger Probe"

The body responds to perceived danger exactly the same as it would in true danger—more so if you perceive that you are too weak, aren't fast enough, can't withstand the threat, or can't handle the loss. Contraction of your blood vessels result in "a cold sweat," the mouth dries, hair raises, the heart beats rapidly, breathing increases, muscles tremble and twitch, the pupils of the eyes dilate, and the sense to do something immediately magnifies.[47]

Much of the science studying the physical and psychological reactions to potential threat was done in the late 1800s and early 1900s by scientists, such as the physiologist, Dr. Ivan Pavlov (1849–1936). Most people recognize him from his studies regarding conditioning, and how the dog's mouth watered when Pavlov rang a bell. But Pavlov also studied how the dog's digestion and salivation completely stopped when there was stress or agitation. Another renowned scientist from Harvard, Dr. Walter B. Cannon (1871–1945), studied the physiological response to perceived threat, fear, and anger. His work was foundational to the understanding of how we physically respond to perceived threats against our survival through what he describes as "fight or flight."

He found that when presented with a perceived or actual threat, our body goes through a series of physiological changes that prepare our body to either have the strength and endurance to fight for our lives—or to freeze or run and flee in order to hide, shrink, or attempt to disappear from threat.[47] And our mind adjusts to assess, and then reacts.

- If you are presented with danger and have a sense that you can handle it, you are more likely to take the risk and expend intense energy to fight.

- If you don't have a sense of ability, you are more likely to freeze, flee, shrink, and hide.

As described by Dr. Joseph E LeDoux, a renowned scientist who studies the brain and the fear response:

"The meaning of the environmental stimuli present is added by the retrieval of memories. If the stimuli are known sources of danger, 'fear' schema are retrieved from memory. My hypothesis, then, is that the feeling of 'fear' results when the outcome of these various processes (attention, perception, memory, arousal) coalesce in consciousness and compel one to feel 'fear.' This can only happen in a brain that has the cognitive wherewithal to have the concept of 'me,' or what Endel Tulving has called 'autonoetic consciousness.'" [46]

Fight, flight, and freeze mechanisms involving the brain and nervous system respond to initial perceptions of the environment in response to memory from your past experience, and self-awareness. This would require a two-part relationship between an assessment of 1) oneself in relation to 2) one's environment. These perceptions merge in the mind to assess "threat." [46, 47]

- The sensitive response to apparent dangers has become so important to the survival of our species that this mode is activated even if the threat is simply suspected or perceived. Our mind "looks out" for danger.

- Survival mode can be triggered even if you experience something as simple as the stress felt when facing a situation in life you feel challenged to handle. Danger doesn't have to actually exist.

- Experience doesn't have to happen. Threats can be triggered by assumptions of weakness and insecurity that presumes you can't handle what it is in your mind you're comparing yourself to.

- Essentially, you have a "danger probe" that uses beliefs and memory about your capacity to evaluate and sense environments, circumstances, or situations to signal a level of threat or danger. **The more insecure you are about yourself; the more likely threat will be alarmed.**

The evaluation of one's capacity, to some degree, makes the triggers of danger a personal experience. Although, as a species we as humans have evolved to be predictable in what we evaluate ourselves by. This is where Maslow's hierarchy of survival needs come in.

He predicted that through tens of thousands of years, we've evolved to be "pre-wired" to feel more insecure with more vital needs to survive. These needs, when vulnerable, determine the priority of our psychological motivations.

Its predictable that humans have some degree of insecurity to handle being seen as inadequate or worthy of exclusion—but more so, they have higher degrees of insecurity to handle loss of shelter and environmental safety, and we are the most insecure to handle threats to food, water, shelter and other physiological requirements for life. Assessments regarding these hierarchy of needs are what ultimately form perceptions of safety and danger.

And because the difference between life and death is all-or-nothing, our perceptions about these things tend to project this sharp reality that has no wiggle room for lenience and grace into how we think. When insecure, the mind distorts to see through a lens that sees reality with perfectionistic all-or-nothing risk. This way of looking at things is the basis of cognitive distortions.

Survival Mode and the Mind

Each and every aspect of survival mode is wired to preserve life with self-defense. When looking at fear of body fat and food, clearly what triggers these mechanisms go beyond being hunted by a tiger and chased by a bear. These are dangers that aren't as easily defined.

These mechanisms and how they manifest psychologically, are best described as *cognitive distortions*. This is how our mind thinks and functions when fear distorts how we perceive, process, and respond to our environment.

> **NOTE:** Cognitive distortions, a concept from Cognitive-Behavioral Therapy (CBT), are biased ways of thinking that occur when a person is in fear or feels insecure with threat. These are psycho-

logical symptoms of flight-or-flight. In other words, when a person is in survival mode, the way she thinks and her attitudes are predictably twisted, and self-centered.

According to evolutionary psychology, survival mode changes the mind to distort the way information is processed to use mental shortcuts and biases rather than logical thinking.[44]

Logical thinking in a time of threat takes too much time; it would be safer to cut corners in order to be safe rather than sorry.

This is like making an assumption about someone's character based on the clothes he wears. In terms of feeling safe with a stranger, a person who is in survival mode would find it easier to compare that stranger's looks to people she feels safe with. It would feel too risky to take the time to get to know them. Clearly this is the case with cultural concepts of body image, such as thin(ner)-supremacy, and the goal of "fitting in."

Another example of this is when animals flee or take flight when they see small movement, assuming it's better to leave and not risk anything. Even if there is no predator, they expend the energy fleeing instead of first taking the risk of gathering evidence. People are the same way. In fear we gather evidence of a problem that might not exist, and we assume the worst. This is common *with the threat of abandonment,* by trying to detect cheating or deception when there is none.[44] This is like thinking that everyone at the beach will look at you, and be concerned with how fat you are, so you make the decision to not go at all. *Better safe than sorry.*

A state of insecure survival shifts the mind to predict, defend, and protect oneself from threat—shifting the mind to perceive everything from a viewpoint of "danger."

People's viewpoints become biased toward perceptions of self-preservation, and focused toward getting what they need to feel safe and protected from what they think is threatening.

In a culture of thin(ner) supremacy, this would drive believers to weight-loss programs, as well as explain why strict food restrictions would ultimately drive dieters to impulsively overeat.

Dr. David D. Burns researched the topic, and in his book, *The Feeling Good Handbook* (1989), he describes these thought patterns. Some of the examples of cognitive distortions described by Burns are:

- **All-or-nothing thinking:** You look at things in absolute, black-and-white categories.

- **Over-generalization:** You view a negative event as a never-ending pattern of defeat.

- **Mental filter:** You dwell on the negative.

- **Discounting the positives:** You insist that your accomplishments or positive qualities don't count.

- **Jumping to conclusions:**
  A) Mind-reading: you assume that people are reacting negatively to you when there's no definite evidence.
  B) Fortune Telling: you arbitrarily predict that things will turn out badly.
- **Magnification or minimization:** You blow things way out of proportion or you shrink their importance.

- **Emotional reasoning:** You reason from how you feel: "I feel like an idiot, so I really must be one."

- **"Should" statements:** You criticize yourself (or other people) with "shoulds," "oughts," "musts," and "have tos."

- **Labeling:** Instead of saying "I made a mistake," you tell yourself, "I'm a jerk, or "a fool," or a "loser."

- **Personalization and blame:** You blame yourself for something you weren't entirely responsible for, or you blame other people and deny your role in the problem.

I've observed that many people who hold themselves to a thin(ner)-supremacy body image, and also are afraid of body fat, are attracted to more extreme diet restrictions, have emotional needs to lose weight that seem to stem from many of these cognitive distortions. Notably true is the magnifying or catastrophizing of their weight, the danger of food, and the difficulty of food restrictions.

But as this distorting, shortcut processing occurs when there isn't actual threat, it can promote confusion, ignorance, irrational thinking, and exhaustive impulsive behavior. It's like when:

- I had an eating disorder and ate "bad" food and could immediately "feel" fat growing on my body.

- A binge eater feels intense panic that she is going to starve to death when she feels bad about her weight.

- A dieter thinks one bite of something prohibited from her diet plan is equally as catastrophic as bingeing, so she binges thinking she already failed with one bite.

- A dieter who is ultra-lean "sees" fat on her body where there is none.

- A person who is perfectly healthy thinks she has to inflexibly omit "bad food" to prevent disease she doesn't have.

This means that even though cognitive distortions might appear wrong and irrational on the outside, they are actually perfectly functioning processes of the mind in survival mode when there's a perceived threat. This is like when a person has repeatedly experienced being attacked, and has seen others get attacked, like in war. It would make sense that the alarm system or "danger probe" in their brain would need to stay turned on and active in detecting and defense against future attacks—above all when environments and situations look similar to past traumatic attacks.

If you've been judged for being too fat, or have witnessed others be mistreated, ridiculed, and rejected because of their larger body, your mind will set an alarm that alerts you when it detects whether or not you're at risk for that type of treatment.

To some degree, this will leave you feeling paranoid that all people are narcissistic thin(ner) supremacists seeking to mock and publicly shun you, and that you must be concerned and aware of what could be wrong with your body, especially in social situations.

Distortions Are Not "Personality Traits"

It's incredibly common for people to assume the symptoms of cognitive distortions are their "personality traits." When I describe perfectionism as an aspect of survival mode manifesting as "all-or-nothing," my clients experience both surprise and relief. *This gives a person hope that she can be relieved of this type of thinking and impulsiveness.*

As I describe to clients the sensations of fear and impulsiveness as an evolved fight-or-flight response to perceived threat, they

typically feel immediate compassion for themselves, realizing they aren't crazy.

Those sensations are what should be expected if restricting food is perceived as life-threatening, if you believe 1) "bad" food will kill you, 2) that gaining weight will kill you, or 3) that people will stigmatize you as a lesser human being and then reject you. These distortions and sensitivities might drive you crazy, but they are there when life feels threatened, and have at some point in evolution benefited our species, otherwise they wouldn't exist.

Ask yourself:

- ✓ Do you assume others are as critical of your body fat as you are?
- ✓ Do you think people are concerned about your weight and what you eat in public?
- ✓ Do you read labels on packaging to make sure you aren't eating "toxic" food?
- ✓ Do you excessively exercise to prevent fat gain?
- ✓ Are you anxious in public, worried that you're being criticized about your body?
- ✓ Do you compare yourself to people's bodies in social settings to see who is the "best" or "worst" in relation to who is the thinnest or fattest?
- ✓ On one hand, does this comparison give you a sense of confidence? On the other hand, does this comparison give you a sense of embarrassment, resulting in the urge to leave or hide?
- ✓ When dieting, do mistakes and deviations from food restriction rules feel catastrophic, or "all-or-nothing?" You either follow them perfectly, or not at all.

Request for my help from a professional woman in her 30's:
I came across your YouTube videos a year ago, and I'm a huge fan of your work. I have tried every diet possible, and it's really left me mentally and emotionally drained. I NEVER stop thinking about food and weight, and I'm obsessed about losing 20 lbs. I stopped doing fad diets about a year ago, but I struggle still with eating to hunger. I have HUGE anxiety around food and have to eat before I leave the house because I don't know if I will have the opportunity to eat out or eat later. And I really do put certain foods on a "superior" pedestal. Pretty predictable, huh?

I think I'm still bingeing because I'm continuing to try to lose weight with the hunger and fullness scale. Therefore, I eat the bare minimum to feel okay, then I either feel unsafe with food or deprived. What do I have to do for this crap to leave my mind?!? I'm so sick of my mind being focused on something as boring as food. I need it out of my mind because I feel like I have no sense of myself anymore. I have no hobbies beyond anything to do with dieting and body image...heck I can't watch a movie without Googling the actress's diet. I have an obsession with protein and fear carbs and sugar. I don't know why it's so extreme, but I've been weight/body conscious (and dieting) since I was 7 or 8 years old. I'm afraid I don't know who I am without it all.

Readers: What part of her experience resonates with you?

1. Has dieting left you mentally and emotionally drained?
2. Is your mind and focus obsessed on your weight and the food you eat?
3. Do you feel unsafe around food?
4. Are you trying to lose weight with "intuitive eating" or eating to hunger?
5. Have you stopped doing all hobbies because of your obsession with diets?
6. Are you curious about what diets famous people do to stay thin?

Chapter 8

The Body in Survival Mode

"Malice literally makes us sick; we are always the victims of our own vindictiveness. Even secret hostile thoughts result in a physiological attack on one's own body."

– Dr. David R. Hawkins, PhD, Psychiatrist and world-renowned spiritual guru

The Physical Experience of Fear

In terms of survival physiology, perceptions of inadequacy, vulnerability to danger, and resulting fear, these all trigger a cascade of involuntary mechanisms that prepare the body to do something about it. We are motivated in some sense to either, freeze, hide, run, or fight, and the body is put into a position to do just that. In situations stemming from perception, this typically starts in the brain.

Apparent danger, and perceived lack of capacity to handle it, initiates the sympathetic nervous system, which is part of the brain, spinal cord, and nerves that regulate unconscious or automatic functions like heartbeat, temperature, digestions, etc.

When the nervous system is stimulated by stress:

- It turns on or encourages organs that are necessary to promote optimal physical exertion.

- The pupils in your eyes dilate.

- The adrenals release the hormones cortisol and adrenalin, both involved in energizing the body with increased heart rate and respiration. This also raises the hair on the body.

- It also breaks down energy stored in the liver to release sugar into the blood stream as immediate fuel for the muscles.

- Blood vessels constrict, altering the distribution of blood away from the abdomen toward the heart, lungs, central nervous system, and the limbs.

At the same time there is resistance, reduced stimulus, or depression of non-important functions during threat. The mouth dries, the gut and intestines immediately stop producing digestive enzymes, peristalsis or contractions of the digestive systems halts, and hunger goes away. Some people experience nausea, or a burning sensation in the stomach.

The more intense the perceived threat, the more incapable a person feels, the more intense the physiological response and the longer the body stays this way.[47] This means that the more fear you experience, the more and the longer the body responds.

These fundamentals of survival-mode physiology were discussed and published in 1927 by Dr. Walter B. Cannon in his book, *Bodily Changes in Pain, Hunger, and Rage*. Dr. Cannon describes how *the body responds to fear with flight—and responds to anger with fight*. He summarizes the physiology of fight or flight and how the body responds to perceived threat and danger as a way to preserve life when you believe life is being threatened.[47]

My Story: Much of what he describes is exactly what I experienced when I suffered with an eating disorder. The fear response experienced when I thought I was gaining weight, and when I ate "bad" food, was as he described: tunnel vision (dilated pupils), rapid heart rate, cold sweats, hair standing up, dry mouth, and the urge to immediately do something physical.

When I was around food, specifically "bad" food or food I felt deprived of, the fear that I couldn't control or handle my urges to eat, immediately triggered this fight-or-flight response, as if I was in a room with a dangerous enemy. At the same time, I'd have an intense desire to taste the food, eat it, and allow myself some grace to enjoy it. It was at this point that I'd either micro-manage every detail of the food in order to stay safe, or I'd negotiate with fear for my desire for food to eat in a way that didn't seem as dangerous. "If I have only two bites, then I'm still safe." Or "If I puke, or exercise, then there's no danger." In a way, these negotiations reduced the perception of threat, which temporarily felt good or safe. But once I took a bite, things changed rapidly, and I'd lose my grip on safety. It was like thinking I'm going to take a couple of drinks from a fresh spring to quench a dehydrated craving for water, but finding that I'm teetering on the edge of a raging river, and have fallen in and was being pulled down a horrendous current I couldn't escape.

Food simultaneously became both life-saving and life-threating.

Like anybody else, I did what I had to in order to hide or to suppress that feeling. Dieting prevented it, eating off plan promoted it, bingeing relieved it, feeling I was gaining weight promoted it, and purging or exercise relieved it. The cycle of dieting, eating, bingeing, purging, and dieting again ran through my mind over and over again.

This is exactly what I experienced, sometimes over ten times a day, which is why with an eating disorder my entire day was hijacked by whatever it took to feel safe and protected. Keep in mind that the amount of exhaustive work of micromanaging food, bingeing and purging, as well as the intense exercise regimens, didn't give me a sense of accomplishment. It's what was required just to feel safe or "normal," and to feel removed from terror. *The eating disorder was both fight and flight, but also my dangerous threat.*

As food restrictions became more and more rigid, the terror around food intensified. The more catastrophic eating off my plan became, the bigger the binges got. The worse the terror became, the more impulsive I needed to purge or exercise. Imagine having a feeling that you are about to get killed, and the only way to feel safe is to binge, not eat even though you are hungry, or to eat but puke up your food, while all the world around you is eating freely, safely, without torment, horror, or obsession.

***That's what it feels like to have an eating disorder.* You're stuck in extreme survival mode against your body and food, as both are necessary to survive.**

Once I understood that for myself, it gave me relief to know I wasn't crazy, but rather doing exactly what anybody else would do under the circumstance. Because I thought food was a dangerous threat to my body image, and my body image threatened access to food, my mind lived in a constant state of fear, anxiety, with the need for controlling behaviors that stemmed from mechanisms derived from survival mode. I was in a constant state of fight and flight. Fighting for food, hiding from weight gain. Fighting weight gain, hiding from food. It was a vicious cycle between two separate survival needs competing to be fulfilled.

Something to contemplate would be if the stress produced when a person is in survival mode changes, depending on whether he or she is in a state of competence in the energy and strength to fight—or alternatively, the energy and endurance to run away and hide. Clearly, there are distinct differences between the choices to either freeze, hide, fight, or flee.

My hypothesis would be that each has a different perceptual trigger based on a person's sense of intrinsic competence and capacity to handle any given situation, that results in a corresponding physical survival reaction.

For example:

- **Freeze:** When in a state of fear, shock and surprise, where there isn't a definitive understanding one way or the other of one's capacity, there might be a freeze response. This anxiety would take mechanisms that are focused on being still, quiet, and shrinking one's self, to disappear into background.

- **Strength to Fight:** When there is a sense of competence to change a threat, the urge would be to fight. Fighting would require a degree of anger or a way to inflate oneself to seem bigger and better than he or she naturally is. This takes a degree of pride, work, and physical energy to exert force. The end goal is being better, stronger, and superior to any threat.

- **Stamina to Run Away:** When there's some confidence but less energy, a more passive way to fight would be to run away or flee the scene. The stamina of mechanisms geared to deny, avoid, repress, procrastinate, place blame, or distract from vulnerable situations would be needed to separate oneself from threat. Over time this would be fatiguing and depressing.

- **Adaption to Hide:** When there's lack of confidence in oneself, but stronger confidence in one's surrounding or systems, he or she might be inclined to hide or "blend in." Energy is directed toward taking in information about one's environment. An alternative mechanism would be to work hard ahead of time to prevent perceived threats.

These are just a few states of survival mode that would have a direct impact on how a person's body physiologically and hormonally responds. Over long periods of time, it would be predictable that there'd be very specific chronic physical adaptations. For many of the people I've worked with, they've been in this state of mind most of their entire life.

All of the people I work with are adults, typically ranging in age from 25–65 years old. On occasion I've had clients in their late teens or even in their '70s. Most people who've sought out my help started fearing food and worrying about their weight in adolescence, so by the time they reach out to me for help, they've been suffering for at least a decade.

These people have been in stress mode with their body and food, in some cases, for over 20, 30, or even 40 and 50 years. These people are chronic sufferers, and that ultimately comes with chronic physical symptoms.

One of the most interesting observations I've made working with hundreds and hundreds of people from the entire spectrum of eating disorders, is that many of these people have similar physiological ailments. There are long lists of dangerous health consequences stemming from excessive purging, bingeing, and starvation.

> **NOTE:** *Eating disorders can affect every organ system in the body, and people struggling with an eating disorder need to seek medical and professional help.*

Besides the obvious cognitive struggles like anxiety, perfectionism, obsessive and compulsiveness, and depression, many of the people I've worked with struggle with a variety of problems like digestive ailments, osteoporosis, low thyroid, autoimmune disorders like Hashimotos, and Polycystic Ovarian Syndrome (PCOS). These issues could be attributed to genetics, environmental adaptations, or a consequence of daily living in stress about one's body and around food, for a long period of time.

When seeking answers to why I regularly observe certain ailments, I decided to look at fear and the possibility that the anxiety experienced every time a person ate might have physiological consequences. I wondered if fear of food might be enhancing these client's health issues. Why do they all seem to have digestive problems, slower thyroid, and sensitivity to high blood sugar no matter what their weight? I will summarize what I found.

Digestion and Fear

In a sea of research articles, every study I found referenced Dr. Walter Cannon, the "king" of physiology, who coined the term "fight or flight." In the first chapter of Dr. Cannon's book, *Bodily Changes in Pain, Hunger, and Rage*, he discusses the emotions of fear and anger, and how they impact digestion.[47]

He goes into great detail describing the observations of other physiologists, like Ivan Pavlov, regarding the impact that fear, anger, and other excitement emotions have on salivation, stomach fluids, and digestion. Dr. Cannon describes:

> *"The conditions favorable to proper digestion are wholly abolished when unpleasant feelings such as vexation and worry and anxiety, or great emotions such as anger and fear, are allowed to prevail... The influences unfavorable to digestion, however, are stronger than those that promote it. And evidently, if the digestive process, because of emotional disturbance, is for some time inhibited, the swallowing of food which must lie stagnant in the stomach is a most irrational procedure. If a child has experienced an outburst of passion, it is well not to urge the taking of nourishment soon afterwards. Macbeth's advice that 'good digestion wait on appetite and health on both,' is now well-founded physiology."*

In his first chapter, Dr. Cannon writes specifically how important the physiology of pleasure is to salivation, gut "watering," and the overall digestibility of the body when the mind is at ease. He described findings from other scientists who found digestion improved with increased pleasure and excitement for food.

> *"Hornborg found that when the little boy whom he studied chewed agreeable food, a more or less active secretion of gastric juice invariably started, whereas the chewing of an indifferent substance, as gutta-percha, was followed by no secretion. All these observations clearly demonstrate that the normal flow of first digestive fluids, the saliva and the gastric juice, is favored by pleasurable feelings which accompany the taste and smell of food during mastication, or which*

are roused in anticipation of eating when choice morsels are seen or smelled... These facts are of fundamental importance in the serving of food."

This information is exceedingly important as it can be related to people who chronically diet and live fearful of, and omit, pleasurable food. They keep away from social gatherings, remove food they enjoy, reduce tasteful dressings, and avoid other aspects of eating such as sharing food as a symbol of love and safety.

People who diet are often afraid to eat "bad" food, to the point that they avoid plates and dishes, and are reluctant to relax around food. The reluctance to face food and relax with the pleasure of food could be a direct symptom of "fight-or-flight" Dr. Cannon describes in his book.

This survival mode around food is incredibly relevant in response to digestion when observing the physical issues typical of chronic dieters, and of people with disordered eating or eating disorders.

Based on the science presented by Dr. Cannon, shaming and demonizing food, even threatening pleasurable food as addictive, could have unintended consequences harming the physical being of those who rigidly support dieting. Chronic dieters and bingers commonly describe having anxiety if they feel hunger, and they panic when around "bad" food. Addressing how this fear of food impacts digestion and the body's ability to properly break down food is vitally important when observing common ailments of people who live by the safety of diets and fear of food.

Dr. Cannon describes in his first chapter:

"Like the peristaltic waves in the stomach, the peristalsis and the kneading movements (segmentation) in the small intestine, and the

*reversed peristalsis in the large intestine all cease whenever the ob-
served animal shows signs of emotional excitement... There is no
doubt that just as the secretory activity of the stomach is affected in
a similar fashion in man and in lower animals, so likewise gastric
and intestinal peristaltic waves are stopped in man as they are
stopped in lower animals, by worry and anxiety and the stronger
affective states."*

Peristalsis is the smooth muscle contractions of the stomach and small and
large intestines that churns the food, helping break it down, and helps push
it through the intestines to later be excreted. Together with reduced secretion
of digestive enzymes, when in fear, anxiety, worry, or anger, the mechanism
of peristalsis shut down. To a dieter who fears food, this ensures poor and
incomplete digestion.

Considering that the fear response completely shuts down digestion, if the
source of threat, fear, and anxiety are negative beliefs about food a person
wants to eat, it would be expected that the individual holding those fear-
based beliefs would also have symptoms of poor digestion. Consider how
chronic dieting and fearing "bad" food can impact digestion over a long period of time.

**When there are years and years of fearing food, you could pre-
dict that chronic dieters have symptoms associated with under-
digested food dumping into the small intestines, gallbladder
distress, poor nutritional absorption, and overall stress to the
entire digestive tract.**

Survival Mode and "Emotional" Blood Sugar

Another important connection dieting has to survival mode, or fight or
flight, and eating disorders, is the fact that with fear and stress the body naturally secretes sugar into the blood stream. In chapter five of Dr. Cannon's

book, *Bodily Changes in Pain, Hunger, Fear, and Rage*, he recognizes the impact that fear and stress have on blood sugar. The main reason for this mechanism is to make fuel readily available for the muscles in case of intense and prolonged demand that you must be very active, like having to run from a bear.

Cannon says,

> *"Great grief and prolonged anxiety during a momentous crisis have been regarded as causes of individual instances of diabetes, and anger or fright has been followed by an increase in the sugar excreted by the persons who already have the disease... In cases of mental disease, also, states of depression have been described accompanied by sugar in the urine... In these cases, the amount of glycosuria (glucose in urine) is dependent on the degree of depression, and that the greatest excretion of sugar occurs in the fear psychoses."*

Personal Story: When I Had Diabetes

After filing bankruptcy and closing the gym, my husband and I moved our family across the country from Idaho to Minnesota. This is where I published my first book, *Weight-Loss Apocalypse*. Over the span of seven years, because of my husband's job change we ended up moving six times, and three of those moves were across the country. When we finally settled back in Idaho years later, we again had health insurance covered by my husband's employer. After I decided to get a blood panel done to check on my overall health, I received a phone call from the doctor's office, explaining that I had diabetes.

I am not considered overweight, I live an active lifestyle, and I don't emotionally eat, over-drink alcohol, or live in fear (I'll never do that again). I do not meet the typical associations to diabetes, in any way. However, it does run in my father's side of the family.

But there's one other thing: I didn't tell the doctor that I had moved across the country three months prior. Or that I moved across the country six months before that, or that we moved nine months before that, and across the country 18 months before that. I didn't tell her that a year before that I filed bankruptcy and lost our home, and for over a year working over 70 hours a week, still struggled to feed my family. And to top it off, I didn't tell the doctor my mother was diagnosed with terminal brain cancer either.

I knew why I was diabetic: radical environmental stress. I knew what the problem was and chose to let my body come down from the stress. A year later, I had the doctor recheck my numbers, and I was perfectly normal and healthy.

Fear of Food and Survival-Mode Physiology

I find it fascinating that the health industry commonly blames these symptoms on certain foods, like bread, without considering the physical reactions that are magnified by the experience of stress and fear. If certain foods have been demonized as "bad," it would be predictable that a person who believes these warnings would have symptoms of fear when they eat these particular "bad" foods.

A valuable scientific study would be to observe blood glucose and the digestive response to eating certain foods, and compare the results between a group of people who judge and fear food, versus a group of people who are indifferent and unemotional about those foods.

I suspect the group who is afraid, ashamed, and judges the food would have higher blood glucose response and less digestion while they eat it. If this were true, there would be a case against the fear-based sales tactics predominantly used by the diet and health industry to get more followers, sell more books, and to manipulate people into changing their diet.

As a reminder of what's described further in chapter 2:

> **Studies show that stress associated with stigma and shame regarding one's weight increases stress induced C-reactive protein levels (inflammatory marker associated to heart disease), blood pressure, cortisol levels, and oxidative stress.1 Among other things, this response increases the susceptibility to fat gain, even when food isn't eaten to excess.**

As well, media exposure to weight stigma, for people who believe it about themselves, showed a significant increase in cortisol production. People who don't think these things, don't have the same response when they are exposed to weight stigma.[2, 3]

> **This means that a person who is ashamed of her weight and agrees she is "bad" because of it, experiences signals of danger when she sees derogatory media about overweight or "unhealthy" people.**

A growing body of research is beginning to question the mind-and-body paradigm, especially the science and research that indicates weight stigma as a significant factor promoting psychological coping mechanisms. Body-fat stigma encourages isolation, overeating, and reduced physical activity, but also a biological sensitivity to weight gain.

A person who supports and holds herself to thin(ner) supremacy ideals will respond to judgment and shame about body fat as if it's a life-threatening enemy or an angry wild animal chasing her down, stimulating the fight-or-flight response. If she thinks she's overweight, she will live in fear, anxiety, and survival mode because of how dangerous her body is perceived, and this danger projects onto food—as if food is also threatening her survival.

If you apply the fight, freeze, or flight physiology described by the pivotal research done by Dr. Walter B. Cannon, these people would predictably have suppressed digestion, higher resting blood sugar levels, and increased activation of adrenalin and the fight response.[47]

> **Imagine the effect that this type of stress a person experiences daily has on a person's mind and body over a long period of time, from childhood into adulthood.**

This alone would make anybody susceptible to hair loss, thyroid ailments, autoimmune disorders, heart attacks, diabetes, weight gain, etc.—even if she isn't overeating. This is exceptionally true when you add the fact that people who experience stigma avoid the embarrassment of being made fun of by isolating themselves.

Exercise and the Need to "Work Fear Off"

According to Dr. Cannon:

> *"If these results of emotion and pain are not 'worked off' by action, it is conceivable that the excessive adrenin and sugar in the blood may have pathological effects."*

He is suggesting that without exercise and physical labor that stress prepares the body for (running from a bear), the body will have to deal with the toxic excess of fuel that isn't balanced with activity. This excess fuel gets converted into glycerol, then into tri-glycerides, and eventually is stored as fuel.

> **NOTE:** This embarrassment and fear of being made fun of has shown reduced motivation to exercise in both children and adults, ultimately promoting elevated blood pressure and increased physiological stress.[13, 24]

When stress is triggered in the brain, exercise can be a much-needed mental and physical relief. Unfortunately, studies have shown that people who feel bad about their weight are less motivated to exercise, in fear of being made fun of. [28] Over time the underutilized energy and fuel promoted by stress might promote pathological effects like a slower thyroid, higher levels of testosterone in women, increases in estrogen in men, adrenal fatigue, and obvious digestive issues and nutritional malabsorption.

If a dieter has life circumstances, like the loss of a job, a death in the family, or marital stress, this would exacerbate her magnified blood sugar and suppressed digestive response, on top of the shame and guilt that she experiences eating "dangerous" or bad food. Add to that a reduction in physical activity due to injury or stress that renders her without the motivation, energy, or tolerance for physical activity, and the physiological sensitivity to weight gain heightens even further.

> **I assume people who are "battling their weight" would have a more exaggerated response when experiencing these types of life stresses, *due to the underlying fear they hold about both their body and food.***

Research correlating the stigma of obesity and internalization of that shame over the course of the last decade—*to the susceptibility of weight gain, stress, anxiety, isolation, reduced motivation to exercise, depression, stress eating, binge eating, psychological and physiological stress factors*—is overwhelming strong.

Combine that with the psychological response showing a significant increase in binge-eating behavior—*no matter what starting weight, age, BMI, race/ethnicity, or socioeconomic factor*—for anyone who experiences and internalizes weight stigma, they are going to end up with obesity.[23, 25, 26]

In other words, for those who believe it, weight stigma increases their personal likelihood of becoming and remaining obese. *The belief in the stigma of obesity alone increases your risks.*

NOTE: Many of my clients have suffered with disordered eating and eating disorders for years before being diagnosed with digestive problems, metabolic syndromes, and thyroid disorders. I ask clients if they've informed their doctors of their eating disorder, and virtually none of them have disclosed that information. In my opinion, it would be advantageous for these medical professionals to know how many of their patients suffer with disordered eating and eating disorders, and why that might be significant information as they seek answers and resolutions to these ailments—especially if the protocol for the patient's ailments are to recommend radical food restrictions. Shaming food and encouraging food restrictions for that reason might actually be promoting their symptoms.

In cultures that worship thin(ner)-supremacy body images, it would be expected that trusting followers would be on high alert when it comes to their body fat and the threat that food poses. When positioned to fear your body, fear other's opinion about your body, and to fear food, it would be understandable why believers would have direct physical symptoms stemming from how the body responds to that fear. If you look at the "epidemic of obesity," it would be better to call it an "epidemic of fat stigma," coming from a plague of narcissistic thin(ner) supremacy.

Ask Yourself:

✓ When experiencing life stress, do you feel sensitive to fat gain?
✓ Have you noticed that when life appears to be out of control, it's more difficult to stay motivated on a diet?

✓ On the other hand, when life seems to be out of control, does doubling down on your diet restrictions give you a sense of safety and control?

✓ Have you ever felt that eating "bad" food was disastrous, no matter what the quantity?

✓ Have you experienced eating "bad" food and thought the resulting damages weren't repairable that day?

✓ Do you recall a time thinking you had to eat perfectly in order to be healthy?

✓ Have you ever thought that order to be healthy you must do cleanses or detox because your body can't process "toxins" on its own?

✓ If so, have you ever considered how the human body survived tens of thousands of years without diets or modern forms of "cleansing?"

✓ What would happen if all forms of food fears, judgment, and rules were blacked out from your life?

"Apart from being exhausted, financially unstable, nearing a mental breakdown, and being fat—everything is great. Thanks."

– Author unknown

Chapter 9

When Both Your Body and Food are Dangerous

"The Ego, however, is not who you really are. The ego is your self-image; it is your social mask; it is the role you are playing. Your social mask thrives on approval. It wants control, and it is sustained by power, because it lives in fear."

– Deepak Chopra, Spiritual Guru

When People and Businesses Sell Fear

As you go through your day today, take notice of how regularly you see articles, advertisement, and programs that use fear to get your attention. When it comes to body image, notice the use of scare tactics regarding toxins, cancer, disease, and death. Chances are, what's being sold are supplements, pharmaceutical drugs, ways to control your environment, and more often than not, food restrictions.

Instead of looking at the entire picture to understand the body's heightened sensitivity promoted by stress, both the diet and health industry classically incriminate food.

Not to say some of the information isn't relevant under certain contexts, but the way information is shared is through danger, threats, and fear, and this type of communication isn't helping matters.

Businesses that sell solutions to these issues get followers' attention by saying things like, *"That food is so bad for you. It's toxic, causes cancer, and it's fattening too. You'll end up with diabetes!"* They omit the truthful complexity of the issue by making it seem linear, or black and white. Otherwise headlines and conspiracy theories wouldn't be as effective at triggering fear that grabs the attention of listener's sensitive "danger probe" and survival mechanisms.

Whether fearing fat or sugar that's been added to food, the pleasure of food they assert is addictive, or has toxins that will kill your body, the viewpoint is singularly looking at a source they want you to think is dangerous.

What these messages are missing is that the body has mechanisms that evolved to survive challenge, illness, changing viruses, and diseases over tens of thousands of years. Over and over again, humans were forced to survive through massive environmental shifts and cataclysms that challenged the body's innate capacity to adapt in order to keep the species alive. We as humans wouldn't otherwise be here.

> **EXAMPLE:** In 2011, my mother was diagnosed at the age of 65 with an aggressive and terminal brain cancer. She was given 6 –18 months to live. She was active in her life both spiritually and physically, she never had a drink of alcohol or coffee, and she never smoked a cigarette. Most of her life was lived in small towns and rural environments. She was a nature-loving person who loved to cook as well as garden, growing her own food. She never dieted because she wasn't willing to sacrifice the joy and taste of real food.

After brain surgery, which took out a large portion of her brain, her activity almost completely stopped. She lost her ability to process how to cook, and her taste for food drastically changed. Before, she cooked all of her own meals. After, finicky, she only wanted fast food. Every morning and lunch, my father would lovingly make a run to the local fast-food chain to get her the muffin, sausage, and egg breakfast, and for lunch an Italian salami and meat sandwich or cheeseburger. Later in the day, she wanted chocolates and ice cream. She craved the same fast foods, day in and day out, over and over again. As a result, my father spent a great deal of money and time putting together nutritional supplements that would provide what her food was missing.

Against all odds, my mother ended up living an additional five years this way, eventually dying in 2016 because of the continued growth of the cancer in her brain. What amazed me the most as I watched her life radically change, was that her body and brain fought to keep her alive until the very last seconds of her life.

In terms of health, her body aggressively fought for the health of her life up until her last few breaths.

When clients discuss how vital it is to eliminate sugar to be healthy, or to be afraid of *"fill-in-the-blank,"* I am reminded of my mother's body surviving years longer than she was supposed to as she ate all the "bad" food. I ask, can we as humans comprehend what is required in any given environment to maintain consciousness and to keep the body alive?

To suggest that food eaten today is catastrophic, clearly indicates a high level of cognitive distortion. Of course, eating less nutritional food over longer periods of time does have negative physical consequences. But eating these types of food with a large variety of other foods could be argued as "healthy." When a person's mind is seeing things through life or death, they can't see this reality though. They literally feel a sense of death attached to foods they fear.

We aren't wired to be open to the vulnerability of death, and in fear, our mind is geared to seek anything that provides the perception of safety.

It makes sense that people who are afraid of the vulnerability of death because of "unhealth" would feel unsafe with food when it's constantly promoted as dangerous. Under the circumstance, anyone would be impelled to seek out information that provides explicit controls, with black-and-white rules to follow. You could say they are in a more intense and heightened degree of survival mode.

However, statements that describe food as toxic or addictive reflect cognitive distortions that are being projected from the minds of those who are in such a state of survival mode. They devote a significant amount of brain power finding and spreading catastrophized fear-based warnings. Unfortunately, this type of zealotry isn't only about food, but it's also about the capacity of the body.

Fearing, shaming, and distorting the facts to make it appear as if food is cat-astrophically toxic no matter how much is eaten, carries the underlying belief that your body can't digest, process, and metabolize food—*that the body doesn't understand how to survive.*

In effect, the message that food is bad is also a message that your body is weak and incapable. You're taught not to trust your own body and its capacity to keep you alive, and that it can't handle the food you want to eat.

Request for help from a woman in her late 40's:
Hi Robin, I am a chronic dieter and have been diagnosed with binge eating disorder. I have followed you on YouTube and am familiar with your work. I have really bad digestion issues and was told I have what is called "leaky gut" with high antibodies, and even SIBO etc. I also have Hashimoto Hypothyroid. Some Hashimoto specialists are telling me the only way to heal is to diet. One part would be to do the modified paleo Autoimmune Protocol and then permanently re-strict all food with gluten and dairy for a lifetime. The specialist warned me that unless I restrict this way, my Hashimoto disease or my thyroid will continue to get destroyed, and I will probably get other autoimmune diseases.

I feel like I have constant anxiety about these foods, and I find that it feels hopeless to restrict them. I know I need to remove dairy and gluten for my health, but I can't seem to control myself. Can a person with autoimmune diseases heal without having to be permanently restrictive with food? How can you "eat to hunger" foods that are dangerous for your body? I can't seem to balance the fact that I shouldn't eat certain foods.

Readers: What part of her experience resonates with you?

1. Do you have an eating disorder and experience digestive problems?
2. Have you disclosed to the doctor who has diagnosed you with your digestive problems that you have an eating disorder?
3. If the doctor helping you knew you suffer from an obsessive-compulsive eating disorder, would they recommend food restrictions?
4. Have you noticed while doing the food restriction protocols the weight loss industry recommend that your binge eating has increased?
5. Has your obsession about food increased since doing food restriction protocols?
6. Is overall stress and anxiety about health and food exacerbating your autoimmune disease?

Believers who proselytize fear of food might think they are helping others avoid illness and death, but instead they are spreading anxiety and inflamed survival mechanisms to those who innocently trust, and don't question the state of mind where these distortions are coming from.

> **When food and your body is thought to be disastrous, it is assumed that the only way to have success is to restrict perfectly: *total abstinence*.**

Therefore eating "bad" food when you think your body can't handle it assumes, even one bite causes damage. Like the all-or-nothing of life and death, food restricted as a way to "survive" would feel the same way. Just a small amount of "bad" food can feel like "death" to your efforts to lose weight or be healthy.

> **EXAMPLE:** Imagine being at the movie theatre, and the popcorn you were raised to enjoy is now considered "bad" because you're told the type of oil and salt used is toxic and bad for your metabolism and hormones. How are you going to feel when friends and family order popcorn for everyone—when you think your body can't handle it? Being around the popcorn might feel as if you are walking on eggshells.
>
> You might rationalize eating just a couple bites. But with these few bites, it can feel like all efforts at "health" have been ruined and there's no point to holding back.

The common reactionary thought is that once those bites are taken and the damage is done, it isn't worth enforcing the strain of food restriction anymore if the benefits have been ruined. For many people, this is the tipping point of a binge or what some people call "emotional eating."

> **The combined impact of perceiving food as "bad" and having a "bad" body isn't improved food restriction; it's increased perfectionism and a higher risk of binge eating and physical symptoms of survival mode.**

For most people who live in fear of food and their body, it would be easier to isolate themselves from food than it is to abstain from it. It feels safer to remove "bad" food from their home, avoid social settings, and fixate on ways to repress hunger.

People who live this way often seek online help with how they can repress not only cravings, but also hunger. They try to motivate themselves by searching out inspirational pictures, stories of success, and "healthy" recipes they think are safe for their body. That's what happened to me—and also to all of the people I've worked with. And in doing so, the issues with fear and anxiety get far worse, and so do the feelings that you're sensitive to weight gain and unhealth.

For people who internalize these fear-based beliefs about food, in regards to weight gain, they are going to experience higher levels of fear about food, and will be more sensitive to fat gain because of that fear-based anxiety.1 In this case, it is like a self-fulfilling prophecy where if you think that food is unhealthy and fattening, then your mind and body will respond accordingly.

> **This is not necessarily promoted by what a person eats, but rather fostered by the fear he or she experiences eating, or being around "bad" food.**

This certainly would make a person's body more sensitive to weight gain when compared to a person of equal size—who is not frightened or ashamed of eating.[22] Unfortunately, the blame is placed on the fragility of the body and the contents in the food, which perpetuates the fear and anxiety experienced when eating or being around that food.

As described earlier, because of fear and stress experienced eating "bad" food, a dieter might have higher blood sugar before she starts eating, and while she's eating her body isn't going to adequately produce digestive enzymes. The body in fear and shame will stop digestive peristalsis for hours, and will simultaneously release stress-and-fight hormones such as leptin, adrenaline, and cortisol. This person is most definitely going to have physical symptoms, notably if he or she doesn't effectively chew the food, which is true of most people during a binge.

> **Is it fair to blame food for physical reactions that are primarily due to primitive mechanisms meant for survival mode?**

Request for my help from a woman in her late 30's:

Hi, Robin, I found your YouTube channel a while ago, and have recently been watching your videos again. I find them so incredibly valuable and thought-provoking. I wanted to contact you just in case you might be able to offer any insight to my situation. But I'll keep it short in case you get a lot of these messages, and don't have time for them.

I've struggled with anorexia and over-exercising for over 20 years, and I'm having a hard time making steps toward recovery. I totally have orthorexia, too, and it's making it exceptionally difficult to get any footing in recovery. My doctor thinks I have celiac, too, given that I for sure have Hashimotos, an autoimmune thyroid disorder, which doesn't seem to be a transient condition ever. I've been gluten free and dairy free for a long time due to this problem, but if I ever recover, I will still need to substitute for gluten, right? To recover, am I to dismiss everything I've read about the role of diet (gluten and dairy in particular) in autoimmunity?

*Everything I've read says these foods are pretty much non-negotiable for someone with Hashimotos, not to mention if I have celiac, and I'm even currently doing an elimination diet to see what else could be causing symptoms. I just want to be free of all this insanity, and I know only I can free myself, but to what extent? I'm deathly afraid to gain weight and have been afraid of food for over 20 years. Now that I have these digestive issu*es, the type of food I feel safe eating is even more restrictive.

There are plenty of substitutes for gluten, but after 20 years of this eating disorder hell, trying to get healthy with these restrictions have made mental recovery next to impossible. I am terrified that if I eat dairy, gluten, or grains that these foods will trigger all kinds of in-

flammation, weight gain and fluid retention, which has happened in the past.

I feel like I've listened to your videos for long enough that I should be able to figure this out. Part of me so desperately wants to be free and eat the foods I loved as a kid before I started starving myself. Part of me is simply not willing to be unhealthy and fat for the sake of being able to eat pop tarts and grilled cheese. So, I feel a little crazy. There are plenty of substitutes. My cabinets are filled with substitutes. I crave freedom, but I can't do it. Ahhhh! I actually really like eating the healthy foods I allow myself, but I end up with hunger that feels endless and insatiable.

I'm afraid if I talk to you, I will end up being okay with being fat, and I really like being thin. Or I will be too stubborn and resistant, and unable to see the light because I can't imagine life outside my miserable cage. I would do anything to be free, except get fat.

It may be worth it for mental freedom, but I can't do it if I immediately get fat/swollen and therefore relapse. I should probably just get to a middle/grey area, where I eat more and just keep out the gluten and dairy, but I still feel so restricted! Thanks so much in advance for any input you may have, and for sharing your brilliance with the YouTube world.

Readers: What part of her experience resonates with you?

1. Have you been obsessed with being thin for over 20 years?
2. Has your obsession with being thin also turned into an obsession with health?

---

3. Do you feel a sense of superiority because of "healthy" eating, even though it isn't satiable and leaves you hungry?

4. Have you noticed with your "healthy" eating you are more sensitive to food, inflammation, fluid retention, and weight gain—similar to sensitivity seen in people who are starving?

5. Are you miserable with your life because you are completely obsessed with your body and food?

When Your Body Threatens Food and Food Threatens Your Body

Thinking they will eventually find safety and freedom, people who support and hold themselves to thin(ner)-supremacy body images dogmatically, live in anxiety about their body and food. Even when their body looks like the ideal, this fear and anxiety doesn't let up.

This seems ridiculous when you consider that the body is responsible for sustaining life, and so is food.

It makes sense that so many people live in fear of their body when the only body that looks safe from discrimination and judgment is a thinner body. They dedicate their life to enforcing food restrictions—but end up living in constant tension as their mind is geared to seek access to food. And when people eventually break down and feed the impulses driving them to eat, they are deemed failures without questioning the influence that diets have on triggering primal urges to eat. In my opinion, this is cruel and inhumane.

I cannot tell you how many people I've met and discussed these issues with who have dedicated most of their adult life, and some of their childhood, to feeling bad about their body and their weight.

It's understandable why multiple generations feared body fat, and thus put their children on diets to help them "battle their weight." They thought they were protecting the future from the judgment, shame, and abandonment that they and others experienced for being unhealthy, diseased, and "overweight."

They were battling for the need to "fit in" and to be worthy of love and belonging. We've had almost a century's worth of experimentation with weight-loss methods and dieting, and we now have accumulated enough trial and error, and unintended consequences that it's time to stop. It's time to recognize that the more shame a person attaches to her body and to herself, the more she will live in psychological pain and suffering.

It's time to stop passing down another generational "battle with weight."

Is Weight Loss Healthy If:

- ✓ It's motivated by an image of being accepted by others?
- ✓ It requires people to obsess over their body, over food, and over exercise?
- ✓ They have a fear response around food, and have to isolate themselves in order to micromanage everything they eat?
- ✓ The food restrictions require people isolate themselves from social gatherings and celebrations?
- ✓ Stress about one's weight stimulates the survival response from the brain that stimulates cortisol and other metabolic reactions that promote fat gain, even when eating is less?

SECTION 3

Courage to Accept the Vulnerable Truth

"Cessation of fear is the result of learning that the source of happiness is within. It stems from recognizing that this source is the joy of one's own existence, which is continuous and not dependent on externals. This results from surrendering expectations and demands on one's self, the world, and others. The thought "I can only be happy if I win or get what I want" is a guarantee of worry, anxiety, and unhappiness."

– Sir David R. Hawkins, MD, PhD

Chapter 10

Letting Go of Dieting and Weight-Loss Methods

"There is nothing wrong with your body, but there is a lot wrong with the messages which try to convince you otherwise."

– Rae Smith, award-winning theatre designer

Turning People Away from a Weight-Loss Program

Emails and requests to work with me come in cycles, with some predictability to it. I usually get contacted to help people prepare for a weight-loss program some time in November and December. These are people who plan to start a diet in January. Predictably, starting in February and throughout March I get contacted by people seeking help with emotional eating and binge eating. They reach out for my help about a month or two after reinforcing a restrictive diet as a New Year's resolution. They feel miserable, dejected, out of control, and ashamed that they've failed their resolution and regained lost weight. The other time this cycle occurs is with dieting that starts up again in the spring and predictably ends in emotional and binge eating during the summer months.

For other people, there is no predictable cycle because dieting and emotional eating is occurring every day, every week, all the time. Those clients typically reach out when they are in a dark space that feels like hell. They find me when searching for information on YouTube about eating disorders. They somehow find my YouTube channel in a sea of available content, like finding a needle in a haystack.

When someone finds my YouTube videos, takes the time to sift through and watch them, and then reaches out for my help, *they are already miserable.*

They've lived in psychological hell for so long that they are willing to listen to hour-long video discussions that bring up high levels of cognitive dissonance, or painful truths they don't want to hear. By the time they request my help, they've been through a cycle of thinking that what I suggest to clients in the videos is terrible, then questioning themselves—if what I'm saying might actually be true; then opening their mind to hear it without denial, rejecting it again; and then realizing more deeply the truth in what I'm suggesting. In order for them to end the misery, they will have to give up all forms of dieting, weight-loss methods, and the endeavor to be thinner.

> ***Message of Hope from a 30-year-old Woman Struggling with Binge Eating****: I found Robin on YouTube and tried to stop bingeing with the use of the hunger and fullness scale. I continued to struggle so I decided to bite the bullet and work with Robin. I like the way she tells it like it is, doesn't placate your issues, and puts your issues in the spotlight. After the first consultation I wasn't sure I was ready to let go of wanting to be thinner. I decided to continue to work with her, and again after a few sessions, I wanted to quit because it was so hard and difficult to face letting go of all the things I wanted to achieve from losing weight. But the more I suffered bingeing and my frequent running back to diets, the more I realized what Robin was saying was the truth. Once I realized I had to let it go, I cried and cried. But it was like a light bulb that switched on, and it was easy after that. It took a good year of work with Robin before that moment happened—and it changed my life.*

The only way to heal is to accept you won't lose the weight you just gained, because you aren't going to diet...*for the rest of your life.* And with that, you'll have to accept permanent weight gain if you continue to binge and eat emotionally. This message can be very confusing to people seeking guidance for weight loss who find my YouTube channel.

On one hand, I'm encouraging people to abandon and become permanently abstinent to all forms of dieting, but on the other hand, I'm considered an expert at a very specific medical weight-loss treatment. How could this be?

If I were to deny the benefits of losing fat when a person has hundreds of extra pounds of body fat to lose, pounds that contribute to significant limitations and physical distress, I would

be ignorant. However, in my opinion, to suggest a person lose body fat without addressing how and why it was gained is far worse.

There is chronic strain that the body handles with:

- Physiological stress stemming from fear of rejection and abandonment.

- Perceived danger through the "badness" of the body and food.

- Physiological and nutritional deficits due to abrupt and prolonged food restriction.

- Survival mechanisms impelling the mind to gain access to food.

- Defense mechanisms agitating the mind to fight for food that's being deprived.

- Shame associated with failing to restrict food and being "out of control."

- The physical strain and stress from excessive food consumption.

- Shame and isolation as the body gains more body fat.

- Physical strain and stress from excessive food consumption before the next abrupt and prolonged food restriction.

- Bouts of extreme exercise, or extreme sedentary behaviors.

- This cycle, over and over again, for years, decade after decade.

To suggest a weight-loss treatment program as a means to heal hormonal imbalances linked to excess body fat without first addressing and stopping this vicious shame cycle would be like throwing gasoline on a raging fire. You'd be adding to and making the problem worse. Especially if a person successfully heals the body and loses a significant amount of weight, but then experiences more severe and catastrophic shame when they revert back to the diet-binge-diet cycle as they regain body fat that they took pride in losing.

For this reason, as people reach out for my help with the medical weight-loss program, I discourage most people from it and suggest they eliminate it as an option.

Until the desire for body images that might be triggering insecurity and danger to your third hierarchy of need are addressed and resolved, I don't recommend any dieting or food restrictions whatsoever.

When I get a call from someone who is already on a diet or weight-loss program, the best advice I can give him or her is to stop monitoring their weight, and to prepare emotionally for when and if weight that's been lost is then regained. My goal is to help participants accept their fear of weight gain in order to discourage them from dieting once a weight-loss treatment is over. The goal is to open their mind to the truth of their body, if he or she were to eat based on the biological rhythms of hunger. You can read more about eating to the biological rhythms of hunger fullness in *Body Supremacy*.

Even with my best effort to help people recognize the suffering that comes with rejecting their body, most people aren't willing to accept the truth. They aren't willing to face letting go of the idea and promises in the mirage of thin(ner) supremacy.

Until triggers for survival stemming from food deprivation and thin-supremacy body images are gone, weight-loss programs might pose risks of more harm for a person's mind and body.

When a person frees herself from the weight-loss dogma, accepts her body unconditionally, faces and accepts others' ignorant disapproval, and she lives in freedom from impulsive dieting and urges to eat emotionally for a long enough period of time, she might be a good candidate for a weight-loss treatment. This is true only if her body also meets appropriate criteria.

NOTE: I believe programs and medical treatments for weight loss are appropriate only for people who are no longer emotionally triggered into survival mode because of fears of "health" or opinions about her body and weight. This would mean—no matter what size, shape, and health problems she has because of chronic fear, shame, and hiding with diet and binge-eating impulses—that she forgives herself, her body, and the belief systems that underlie the shame she had about her body. She would have to give the concept of thin(ner) supremacy and "health" grace, so that she no longer holds herself and others to it in fear as if it's a survival need.

In doing so, opinions about her body and about her worthiness of love and inclusion lose power and becomes irrelevant and non-threatening.

Giving the body-image beliefs grace means they are given lenience, and to do this those beliefs must be questioned. The concept of thin(ner) supremacy must be looked at and recognized, not as a superior belief to be aspired to, but rather as a cruel ideology that leads to a life of psychological misery and physical pain, remarkably when it requires chronic food restriction. Body images that were internalized need to be externalized, so that a person's mind and body can get relief from the cognitive distortions and pressures of survival mechanisms. So they can become open-minded to the body.

She'd have to leave the cult of thin(ner) supremacy in order to accept her body unconditionally. Once this process is fully and completely done, then she would be considered as a candidate for a medical treatment that promotes fat loss, and only if her body meets criteria that would merit the risk of food restrictions.

With guidance, only then would a person be able to experience the psychological strain of lowering their food intake with less risk of being triggered into feelings of fear, deprivation, and rebound urges to cycle between dieting and bingeing again.

Even if a person has accepted her larger body unconditionally and is living free from the cycle of dieting and emotional eating, if her body reduces in size and weight, she will need to accept her thinner body unconditionally too if she wants to keep her freedom from the cycle of dieting and emotionally eating. *This means she'll need to accept the potential for weight regain after weight is lost,* otherwise she'll lose the freedom of her mind to instead focus on defending and preserving her thinner body. Her energy will be harnessed toward controlling food instead of living her life.

In order to hedge that risk, there is a process I take people through prior to considering a weight-loss treatment that requires food restrictions as an appropriate form of physical rehabilitation or hormonal therapy. I call this part of the process the Mind of the Mind:Body Method, which is described in detail in *Body Supremacy.* But prior to working on this method, people must be willing to give up all forms of dieting and control intended to prevent weight gain or to encourage weight loss.

Message of Hope from a Woman in her 50s Struggling with Body Image and Emotional Eating: *If I hadn't stumbled upon your*

YouTube channel, I could have easily stumbled upon a diet, and I'd still be suffering in the same crazy cycle. I've learned so much from working with you, and because of that, my life has had major changes. I can say that I am much happier now that my weight doesn't define me, even though I was depressed about it for decades. I don't carry judgment about how I'm supposed to be, and the critical nature of what "beauty" is supposed to be. And I am no longer wasting time, energy, and money worrying about my weight or the food I'm eating. Thanks to your wisdom and help, I don't label food as good or bad anymore. I'm so grateful to have found you and this freedom.

Giving Up Diets and Weight-Loss Methods

When most people reach out for help, they aren't in the "controlled" weight-loss state of their misery. They don't ask for help until they are eating emotionally, bingeing, or "out of control." To help stop the "feasting before famine," a person must first remove the impending "famine." For some people, this is removing the idea that they're going to start a weight-loss program. For others it's removing the idea they are going to remove sugar from their diet tomorrow, or get back to carb free, or that they are going to do intermittent fasting. *To address the emotional aspects of body image, the food restrictions must be surrendered.*

Dieting is the reason why a person's first hierarchy of need is threatened while living in and surrounded by food that is in abundance.

> **Like a bear preparing for hibernation, her state of mind gets stuck on the "pre-famine setting" where she's supposed to eat in anticipation of being deprived for extended periods of time. It's a primitive mindset that clearly doesn't make sense in a world saturated with food with no actual famine in sight.**

When a person commits to reinforcing an artificial famine, excessive eating ahead of time makes complete sense. It would be expected that a person would experience activated primitive defense mechanisms urging her to impulsively overeat while food is available, before and after she diets—even more so when the stress of dieting intensifies as her body gets bigger and bigger.

I ask clients who regularly binge: *"If it was impossible to lose the body fat that is gained after bingeing, would you still binge?"* Over the past 10 years in all of my discussions with people suffering with eating disorders, not one person has said, "Yes, I would binge anyway."

For people who binge and emotionally eat, dieting is the most powerful enabler and reason behind rationalizing, bargaining, and justifying excessive food consumption when there is no physical need. *Most overeaters don't consciously know this because they've always assumed and were told that food is the problem.*

Without a diet there wouldn't be:

- *Feelings of failure, shame, and guilt attached to bending the diet rules.*
  Not only do diets teach the concepts of "good" and "bad" food that promotes all-or-nothing thinking when it comes to food restrictions, but diets supply the black-or-white rules which require negotiations in order for people to feel they deserve and have earned the right to indulge. Without guilt for wanting to break the rules of a diet, a person wouldn't need to use emotions as a way to bargain for her right and entitlement for food. Emotional eating is, in effect, eating that's been negotiated for with the rules of a diet's restrictions.

- *The need to argue for, and rationalize with emotional reasoning, the freedom to eat.*

Having to negotiate for food strengthens emotional bonds with food that have nothing to do with hunger or physical need. Food is eaten to celebrate, entertain, pacify, hide, avoid, distract, defend, repress, deny, decompress, retaliate, resent, punish, sooth, calm, procrastinate, etc. Some of these reasons for eating are normal and shouldn't be alarming. But if a person has to justify and negotiate with her dieting rules in order to repress guilt for wanting to eat, the amount of food she'll end up eating will be as large as the degree she negotiates.

Having to reason for food as if it's "forbidden fruit," inflates its importance.

- *A way to fix the consequential fat gain that results when food is eaten excessively for emotional reasons.*
  I believe that emotional eating arises because dieting is used to fix the physical consequences, as if it's a "rescuer" and prevents people from having to take responsibility in the moment, and for the long-term aftereffects of fat gain. Without a diet, a person would have to ask herself if she's willing to continue to eat as an emotional coping mechanism if she has to take responsibility for what that will do to her body, having to permanently live with the weight-gain consequences. Without a diet to enable illusion that weight gain will eventually be removed, the impulse to overeat is forced to slow down.

She'd have to accept and permanently live with the consequences, which would mean she isn't a victim of her body. Her body is a victim of her unconscious rejection of uncomfortable emotions as she accepts emotional eating as a safer alternative.

Ultimately, as dieting makes food a central focus in a person's life, so do the limitations of his or her growing body. People develop such a reliance on food to manage their day-to-day emotional needs that they are stuck between 1) the anxiety about their growing weight, 2) the anxiety about eating food, and 3) the anxiety about the life stress that desperately needs food to function.

People live in constant search for food while simultaneously experiencing constant shame when they eat, as there's mounting pressure to restrict food the more weight they gain.

As the body gets larger and larger, so do the restrictions placed on a person's life. She doesn't travel, date, exercise, pursue activities that require physical exertion, or socialize. This isolation from freedom in life and self-exploration puts even more pressure on food to replace pleasures and joys in life as the pressure increases for her to lose weight. Ultimately, the only way out is to:

1. Quit all forms of food morality and food restrictions that are stimulating and pressurizing the impulse to overeat. Permanently removing food restrictions and allowing access to food, without guilt and shame and having to beg and plead, will remove the sparkle and "specialness" of food as it is no longer "forbidden fruit." However, the only way to truthfully surrender all forms of dieting is to accept the way your body is without expecting it will ever get better.

2. Accept that you will never lose weight, and that future weight gain will never get fixed, in order to reconcile the facts and truths about what will and has happened to your body. By accepting the truth of what has happened to your body, you are accepting responsibility for the relationship you've had with food that enabled your weight gain. Because there is nothing to excuse or fix the consequences, moving forward you'll need to awaken to and take full re-

sponsibility for the emotional bonds you've developed with food.

3. Address insecurity and feelings of weakness that are an inevitable consequence when giving up a co-dependent emotional relationship with food. As eating becomes an emotional strength when learning how to handle stresses in life, emotional confidence independent of food goes through a weakening process. Without eating you'd feel exposed, immature, weak, and in fear of situations that are perceived as too much for you to handle. This is why dieting is such an important rescuer when it comes to the need to eat emotionally.

Diets give you a sense that you can eat freely for emotional needs without having to accept the consequential weight gain.

Without a diet, you're forced to examine emotional eating. And without emotional eating, you'll have to develop a sense of emotional strength, and this requires you accept and allow your weakness to work, even if it isn't strong enough. Ultimately, this takes courage and willingness to fail.

If all forms of dieting, food restrictions, food judgments, and weight-loss methods are removed from being an option, a person who eats food to compensate for emotional insecurities would have to face the truth of how those dysfunctional relationships impact her body.

Diets provide the illusion that emotional eating consequences don't exist, or they don't have to be addressed because they'll eventually get fixed or taken care of.

Many people know they've gained weight and that their clothes don't fit anymore, but because they've committed to fixing those consequences "in the future," they live in a state of denial about what has happened. If they knew the accumulated weight gain was going to be permanent, would they continue to enable themselves to emotionally lean on food the same excessive way? Probably not.

> **Overeating is enabled by the promise that someday the consequential weight gain will get fixed. It might not get fixed today, tomorrow, next week, or next month, but someday when life isn't so distracting and hard, the diet will be easier, and the weight gain will go away.**

When wanting to emotionally eat, *but without a diet to rescue you from the resulting weight gain,* you have three choices:

1. Eat to cope and willfully accept the fat gain as a permanent consequence.

2. Refuse to eat to cope, and instead, find a new way to distract or avoid the underlying issues. Instead of eating, you find a different compulsive coping mechanism, like shopping, gambling, cleaning, etc. This type of transfer is very common when instead of facing the underlying issue, a person quits one way of coping and replaces it with another. Some examples of how people transfer from one coping mechanism to another are by going away from:
   ✓ Smoking, towards eating/dieting body-image controls.
   ✓ Alcoholism, towards religious controls.
   ✓ Religious controls, towards eating/dieting body-image controls.
   ✓ Body-image eating/dieting controls, towards cleaning and organizing controls.

(Fill in the blanks) _____ towards _____.

3. Refuse to eat to cope, or to cope in other ways, to instead intentionally experience the anxiety, insecurity, and sense of weakness that develops as you face emotions that have been avoided in fear of not being able to handle them. This takes humility and courage.

As dieting is rejected and emotional eating is surrendered, it is inevitable that a person will need to intentionally face the vulnerabilities of life as anybody would when going through a strengthening and an emotional maturing process. In the end, all of this requires that you accept the body as it is, as it should be, and all it will be without dieting and without a dysfunctional relationship with food.

Grieving the Loss, Acceptance, and Letting it All Go

To help clients get a sense of what it would be like to be removed from their obsession with controlling food as well as the drive to overeat, I discuss the option of permanently giving up all diets and judgments about food. I ask:

What would it feel like if you never had to diet for the rest of your life?

Almost all of the people I pose this question to feel immediate relief—but without food restrictions they realize they'll never lose weight again, and that terrifies them. Accepting the vulnerability of their body fat without having control over it seems impossible.

MY STORY: When I suffered with an eating disorder, the idea of being liberated from food restrictions made me panic. My immediate response was concern about gaining weight, as well as the irrational binge episodes I experienced every day. *I assumed that without a diet, there wouldn't be anything to control over my urges to overeat or binge.* But when I questioned if that assumption was true, I recognized that the only reason I binged was because I felt bad and guilty when I ate…because of the rules and beliefs of the diet.

Without a diet, the fear, guilt, and shame that triggered a binge wouldn't exist, and neither would an escape from the physical consequences if I chose to continue to do so. The assumption that I'd binge out of control without dieting was the opposite of the truth. The truth is I didn't want to binge anymore, and I didn't want food to be the central focus of my life. Without dieting, the bingeing episodes would disappear.

With this way of thinking, accepting you'll never diet again means you'll never be thinner, which can feel like accepting a life of emotional and physical misery. This makes dieting seem virtuous, despite the agitation to overeat and the stress about eating that food restrictions habitually trigger.

This is like being backed into a corner where there's pain and suffering, no matter what direction you turn. You're either miserable as emotional eating and dieting has hijacked your life, or you're emotionally pained by having to face reality and remain in a perceived undesirable heavier body.

It's inevitable that when you give up the safety of weight-loss programs (including exercise you've done to balance out food intake) and dieting, that you will have to face the dangers those behaviors repressed and protected them from.

What comes up are feelings of:

- Terror as you'll be unprotected and publicly seen in the truth of your body.

- Exposure as others are openly allowed to have an opinion. You are giving people the freedom to think what they want, without manipulating their viewpoint by professing you'll lose the weight some other time. This is like "coming out of the closet" as a fat person. You are letting your fatness be known, without an excuse.

- Embarrassment for being exposed as a fraud and a failure.

- Fear of being alone.

- Sadness because of the loss.

The battle with weight is in fact a battle to remove fear and embarrassment about your body, that ultimately creates a back-and-forth tug-of-war between dieting and emotional eating. The only way to recover would be to disconnect one from relating to the other, and then to surrender the benefits you get from both. You'd have to accept the truth of your body.

Most people describe incredible sadness once they've come to accept the loss and the end of their dysfunctional relationship with food, dieting, and a thinner body. This sadness is very different from what they experienced previously, which was self-pity, anger, and victimhood. This sadness feels like the loss of war, or a permanent death.

This is like realizing and admitting your marriage has failed, and that divorce is necessary. You must let go and grieve "as it's gone," the good times and the fantasy of what you thought the relationship could be. And despite the immense freedom and relief that comes from ending a tortured existence, there is loss, and with grief, eventually comes acceptance. Acceptance means you fully grasp the loss and have surrendered to it.

When quitting all diets and forms of weight loss, people aren't necessarily sad about the loss of those cruel behaviors, but what they are pained about is the loss of what these behaviors gave to them *emotionally*.

Those who quit dieting:

- Are actually grieving safety, protection, being in spotlight, "fitting in," and a sense of purpose they thought being thinner would bring them.

- Are sad about the loss of the idea of who they wanted to be, and a life concept they thought would bring pride, confidence, joy, and freedom.

- Are mourning the only things they believed they could control and feel good about in their life.

- For many people, they are letting go of the only way of life they know and understand.

Although, when they realize and clearly see they will never recover from the torment, isolation, darkness, and terror of being alone unless they also surrender the benefits, they are presented with a choice.

When the misery of being obsessed with food and dieting surpasses the fear and anxiety of being rejected, *maybe not "fitting in" is the solution you've been looking for.*

You could keep the known benefits of the body image, dieting, and emotional eating, but you are consciously choosing to suffer. Or you could willfully surrender the benefits, and you'll be set free *from both*. But being set free from both would open you up to vulnerability and exposure as you're presented with a new existence that is limitless and has immense freedom and independence from having to be and do what others want. This is like escaping a totalitarian religious cult, *even though you have no concept of who you are or how to function outside of it.*

This means you are leaving everything you know behind, to enter a new life you know nothing about.

All this requires is courage and humility to face and accept the truth of who you are and what you want in life. When you open yourself up to truthfully answer these questions, leaving the cult of thin(ner) supremacy doesn't seem so impossible anymore.

> *Message of Hope from a Woman in Her 60s Struggling with Body Image and Emotional Eating: I met Robin after someone recommended that I read her book and watch her YouTube videos. After hearing her talk to other people struggling with emotional eating, I decided I wanted her help. The work we did together was unbelievable. Robin, thank you for helping me realize my relationship with food was connected to other aspects of my life. I learned so much about myself, and it has been life changing. It has been over five years since we've worked together, and I am still free from dieting, emotional eating, and worrying about my weight.*

Chapter 11

Leaving the Cult of Thin(ner) Supremacy

"As a doctor, let me tell you what self-love does: It improves your hearing, your eyesight, lowers your blood pressure, increases pulmonary function, cardiac output, and helps wiring the musculature. So, if we had a rampant epidemic of self-love then our healthcare costs would go down dramatically…this isn't just some little frou-frou new age notion, 'oh love yourself, honey!' This is HARDCORE science."

– Dr. Christiane Northrop, author and authority in women's
  health and wellness

Giving Up Being Thinner

For most people, it isn't until they reach complete and total exhaustion, fatigue, and misery with the process of dieting and bingeing, and re-dieting and bingeing, that they are willing to face the reality that maybe they should give up dieting and accept their body in order to start living again—even when it will be criticized and judged. In essence, they are willing to accept failure, forgive themselves, and move on. But when your body has gained a significant amount of size and weight, this process is very difficult.

For a person who has gained more body fat than she ever thought she'd allow, it seems as if dieting is the only way to 1) rescue her from feeling out of control with food, 2) remove the weight she's already gained, and 3) protect her from gaining even more weight. Although, if she took a step back to look at how dieting has enabled her dysfunctional relationship with food, she'd see that dieting has been a primary source of strain, anxiety, and shame about eating that underlies the emotional charge behind the drive to over-consume.

The hardest part of recovery for most people is accepting that to stop bingeing she'll need to stop dieting, which means she'll have to accept her fears and assumptions that without a diet she'll:

- Never lose weight again.
- Have to accept her current weight and size, and every aspect of it that she doesn't like.
- Gain weight and could get even bigger.
- Regain the weight lost after the most recent diet.

She'll have to accept her rubbing thighs, her aching knees from extra pounds, and the fear that she might die of every issue/threat that the weight-loss industry uses in order to scare their followers. According to the weight-loss industry, it is presumed you'll be unhealthy, die early, will never get married, won't have children, your loved ones will abandon you, and you'll be alone forever.

The fear thoughts are innumerable, and those fear thoughts bring about even more fear thoughts, all of which feel like a tsunami wave of death you can't handle.

And to make matters more difficult in a culture that shames and stigmatizes body fat, accepting your weight and size when you're considered "too big" or not thin enough would be like allowing others to judge you and dismiss you as an inferior, insignificant, and lesser human being.

When it seems that losing body fat is the only way you'll feel good about your life and be confident in yourself, not going on a diet to rescue yourself would go against strong survival instincts demanding you do something to protect yourself from being judged and discarded like a piece of trash. These fears come across as truthful and realistic, and when there's an easy way to fix, escape, and repress them, it doesn't make sense to accept them without self-defense.

Signals of danger awaken primitive fears of being alone, as if you'll never experience happiness and joy again, or that without a diet your life might as well be over. For many people, letting go of disordered-eating behaviors feels as if your life will be irreparably damaged or permanently disfigured—even though the dieting and resultant emotional eating and bingeing destroy both your body and the freedom of your life.

When Being a Martyr Keeps the Misery Going

It's easy to feel sorry for yourself for having to let go of these behaviors, even though life with them is full of shame, fear, horror, darkness, isolation, and disconnection from life. You feel like a powerless victim scratching at the surface to get away. Having a "poor-me" pity party, as if you're a martyr for having to recover from the miserable cycle of shame, dieting, emotional eating, and shame again, is a last-ditch effort to stay attached to chasing the mirage of being thinner and worthy of love, even though it's incredibly abusive and harmful to your life.

Part of the problem is that it appears as if the fear, negative judgments, and feelings of victimhood and ruin will be permanent, and as if the feelings of emptiness and loss will be unrelenting for the rest of your life.

Whereas dieting provides some sense of hope or possibility for happiness—despite the fact it is only a fantasy or mirage. It seems as if you have only two choices: 1) vulnerability, fear, and assumed pain or 2) a hopeful fantasy of weight loss with the predictable misery of dieting.

On one hand, you could endure a tortured existence, abusing yourself so you don't have to face your fears or the fact that you don't think you can handle them. Or on the other hand, you could refuse to respond to that fear, and face excruciating terror and loss that feels like it will kill you. For this reason, it feels as if the abusive behavior that exists between dieting and emotional eating are inescapable.

Most people feel safer in their dysfunctional relationship with food than they do the vulnerability of freedom, even though it ruins their health, body, relationships, and life. Before you know it, 1) you're either binge eating as a feast before the next famine, 2) obsessing over your next diet, 3) exercising in the middle of the night, or 4) seeking a bathroom or trashcan you can puke food into. However, being a slave to these behaviors eventually becomes hopelessly miserable and is without reward, *and the only way to recover is to give it up.*

There is freedom and peace in facing the vulnerable truth to humbly admit complete and total failure, without blame, self-defense, or excuse. It means you are liberated from having to fight to prove otherwise, and free from having to defend yourself from threat.

What Happens When Being Thinner Isn't an Option?

When I have clients visualize what life would be like if they had to live with a disability, like losing the ability to walk or becoming blind, I have them ponder what would happen to the grievance they now hold about their body fat.

More often than not, clients find it easier to grieve, accept, and adapt to permanent physical disability in their mind than they do to forever stay overweight, or obese. To them, having a physical disability isn't a choice that can be remedied, but having more body fat can be fixed.

When having the option of changing a fatter body to a thinner body, a person doesn't have to accept her weight or surrender her ideal body image, and can keep her positioned to be negative about her body. I have found that catastrophizing, magnifying, or turning up the negative volume towards body fat increases when people have the option of changing their weight. For this reason, clients have a hard time accepting *they will never lose weight again.*

In spite of this, if they can wrap their mind around making being thinner not an option, like losing a body part, they did foresee a grieving process, similar to what it would take to accept the death of a loved one, or a permanent physical limitation like losing their legs. Their position would change from denial, to anger, feeling sorry for themselves, feeling worthless, then to sadness, and finally to acceptance.

What Would Happen to Body Image if You Went Blind?

One way I help people feel this freedom is to intentionally visualize what would happen to their grievance with their body if they became permanently blind. Surprisingly, many of those people find the idea of being blind relieving, freeing, and liberating, as if losing their eyesight gives freedom from having to care or worry about their weight.

Not only does being blind make the negativity about body weight trivial by comparison, but it makes criticism about the way a person looks irrelevant. Being blind gives people freedom from being defined by looks to "fit in" as well as internalized body images. They get a feeling of what it would be like to connect to their surroundings with their other senses, and it gives them relief from being so intensely self-centered about the way they look.

If they can black out or go "blind" to body image, they can experience freedom from being defined by how their body is positively or negatively perceived visually. This gives them a sense of how they'd relate to their body if they could accept it exactly how it is, as if they are blind to "thin supremacy."

From this acceptance I noticed the intensity or volume of people's dissatisfaction made a dramatic change. They'd calm down and recognize that, in the grand scheme of life, their body *was actually pretty good.* Their issues weren't as bad or catastrophic as they made them out to be, and the body they currently live in is manageable, and worthy of gratitude. Often people would respond with intense relief, as if having to be the same weight would allow them to move on and free their life from the pressure and misery of having to devote their life energy to dieting and fixing their body. This is the freedom they thought they'd get after losing weight.

My goal is to help people realize freedom doesn't exist with being thinner, but with accepting the vulnerability of their body.

This made me question and look at how the perceived changeability of the body, in relation to idealized body images, serves as a potential factor that increased, and even promoted the intensity of distortion and dissatisfaction people had with their body. In a state of agitated survival mode, giving people flexibility to change their body automatically promoted a socially more accepted body image that's better than what they have—increasing discontent, distress, and for some, disgust with their current body. Having to face the loss of what they wanted, and to face acceptance instead, isn't easy, particularly when they have the option of continuing to pursue the social benefits they think weight loss would give them.

To let go of idealized body images of thinness would require that a person voluntarily accept the loss of what she wanted and what would benefit her by losing body fat. Freedom gained from relinquishing a "superior" body image comes at a price. Like a contract, the costs must be consciously agreed upon. Even if the feared costs aren't guaranteed, they must be entirely accepted in order to relieve oneself from caring about and defending herself from the slightest possibility.

Examples are:

- If a person attached being thinner to the opportunity to find a mate and get married, giving up being thinner would feel like she's giving up partnership and marriage, and that could potentially mean giving up having children too. It's not that she has to remove her desire to get married, but that she isn't willing to sacrifice mind and body for someone else's gratification.

- If being thinner provides parental approval, proof that she isn't a failure, or safety from feeling judged, then she has to accept parental disapproval, being thought of as a failure, and judgment. The key here is eliminating body images from being defining factors in how she personally identifies her worth, even if important people in her life believe otherwise.

- If being thinner gives her a sense of safety and permission to eat emotionally, to accept her body would mean she'd have to accept the physical ailments and limitations that are a consequence of overeating as a coping mechanism.

A person must develop enough self-worth and respect for his or her life to recognize the cost of gaining other's approval, through narcissistic concepts of body image that are unnatural and unrealistic. Nobody should have to live in continuous misery because of dieting, in isolation from food, and obsessed about her weight and size in order to provide someone else the momentary pleasure of thinking she's attractive or "good enough."

The goal is that people become indifferent to other's approval or disapproval in order to free their focus and direction in life to be self-determined.

For many people who believe in thin(ner) supremacy, accepting their body as it is with the fat it has, feels not only cruel but impossible.

They think the only way to feel good and comfortable with their body is if it's thinner. They put their entire life on pause to instead focus, devote energy and mind power to dieting, monitoring food, and measuring their size and weight. Without the option of being thinner, they assume their life will be doomed, and they will be forced to live in hiding forever.

They think they wouldn't go out in public; they wouldn't attend parties, travel, or go to the beach ever again. People assume if they had to be overweight the rest of their life, that their life would be worthless—*that they are worthless.*

However, when they can no longer tolerate a life of misery with suffering from continuous anxiety about dieting, obsessiveness and fear about food, bingeing, starving, and hiding because of the shame attached to their weight, the only thing a person can do is look at diminishing her need to be thinner.

Letting go of thin-supremacy body images have the benefit of never having shame while eating, which is inherent to judgmental dieting.

You no longer have to fear about having one bite too much, eating at the wrong time, or eating something on the "bad" list of foods. What you eat will no longer make or break how you define your day.

I regularly ask new clients how it would feel, and what would happen if they were relieved permanently from having to lose weight. What would it feel like to erase "be thinner" and dieting from their list of things to do, forever?

Acceptance removes the perceptual distortions attached to the conditions of their body and, for many people, brings about a calm, peaceful freedom, expressly when they realize by permanently accepting their body as it is, they end their "battle with weight." It is then that people understand they would, in fact, go to the beach, travel, and go to parties. They wouldn't have to put their life on pause for anything anymore.

For some people, they've put their life on hold for most of their entire life while at war with their body and food. Losing weight and dieting became their purpose in life, and experiencing a sense of freedom from it feels intensely liberating, and for some, like a rebirth to a new life.

The fantasy that a dieter is chasing when she visualizes the benefits of losing weight is the freedom she'd allow if she could accept her body. But the problem isn't her body, it's the fact that she thinks she has to be thinner to experience that acceptance. But if being thinner wasn't an option, or could be removed from her life, acceptance can happen no matter what size she is.

It is at this point that people can see that having to lose weight or be thinner isn't a necessary condition in order for them to be happy, to be loved, or to feel good about themselves. They realize the problem isn't their body, but rather the attached freedom and happiness to the ideal body image internalized in their head. *They comprehend it's time for them to leave the cult of thin(ner) supremacy.*

> *Message of Hope from a 35-year-old woman: I've been overweight most of my life, starting in the third grade. I remember feeling confident at first, but after hearing comments from kids at school, I began to feel shame, and like something was "wrong" with me. My mom started going on diets with me to solve my "problem." I hid food at home and snuck cookies when no one was looking. Nothing worked for long, if it worked at all. I went to a group class for overweight kids where we had to weigh in front of everyone in this huge room, which was mortifying. When I was in high school, I got pretty thin.*

> *I met my first husband, who always tried to monitor and control my diet and exercise, no matter how thin or heavy I was—I was never good enough. I went to counseling when we divorced, but couldn't seem to get to the heart of my eating issues. I became discouraged, and quit going.*

> *I continued to gain weight. Two years ago, I weighed 297 pounds at my heaviest. After a heart-to-heart with my cousin where I confessed my intense, debilitating anxiety and self-loathing, she told me about Robin. I started listening to Robin's videos on YouTube, read her first book* Weight-Loss Apocalypse, *and it was like she'd somehow managed to get inside my head, see all the things I'd been thinking and feeling my whole life, and then verbalize and address them all.*

> *I had one session with her after I'd been listening to her for over a year. At that point, I had lost some weight, but after binge eating*

again, I had gained almost all the weight back. I was so ashamed, but the session with Robin helped me set my perspective right again, because she helped me see how fear about weight gain strained how I felt about food, and how that triggered bingeing again. She helped me forgive myself.

However, I still struggled with extreme shame, depression and anxiety about my body, food, and life, until recently. One day I just reached the end of my emotional rope. I was in the shower (where all the deepest thoughts happen), and started crying and wallowing in despair. I was so unhappy, and was so tired of feeling that way.

And all of a sudden, it hit me. If my beliefs about myself were making me this miserable and unhappy, then why didn't I change them? No one was forcing me to feel or think this way about myself but ME. Beliefs aren't set in stone! They aren't hard facts, they're just things I think are true! I'd seen that I was wrong about other things in my life and had changed my perspective, and therefore my beliefs, about those things, and I realized there's hope for me in this body image thing too.

I got out of the shower and stared at my naked body, poked and prodded all the parts I was disgusted by, but this time looked at them without judgment. I got dressed and journaled every single thought and excuse I could come up with to stay in the old thin-supremacy mindset. I let myself go fully into all of that without shame or judgment for the first time ever. I paid attention to myself, and respected and listened to myself.

I realized that I have a choice—I can choose to put those thin-supremacist sunglasses on every day and view myself and everyone else through them, and feel shame and misery and victimization. Or I can take those glasses off and see the light—see the beauty that's all around me, and the beauty that I AM, just the way I am, and be happy. I can choose to accept what is, and let go of the rest. As long as I'm breathing, there's hope, and something to be thankful for!

Thank you Robin, for helping me see that I had a choice, and could accept and take care of myself.

Chapter 12

Accepting the Vulnerable Truth

"A surrendered person can eat anything or go anywhere and is no longer subject to fears of contaminants, pollutants, drafts, germs, electromagnetic frequencies or food dyes. Our perception of the body shifts…This shift of perception is from 'I am the body' to 'I have a body.'"

– Dr. David R. Hawkins, *Letting Go: The Pathway of Surrender,*
   page 24

Time Wasted and Freedom Lost

Imagine living this way for twenty, thirty, or even forty years of your life, being defined by your inability to lose body fat and sustain starvation long enough to achieve anything. In order to earn acceptance into a culture—one that encourages totalitarian concepts of thinness that requires starvation—it wouldn't be surprising when there's a tendency of disordered eating in those that dogmatically believe it.

This devotion and dedication of life to striving for goals that are inherently unrealistic, eliminates freedom to have other hopes and dreams that might actually be more emotionally and psychologically fulfilling. In essence, people are encouraged to chase unreachable standards in order to prove they are worthy of love and belonging, and they think by doing this they'll have confidence to live life in freedom the way that they want to.

> **The truth is, making unreachable standards the "gatekeeper"**
> **to acceptance, love, and belonging is a trap that wastes large**
> **amounts of energy and time, and loses freedom in life.**

Many of the people I've worked with in their fifties, sixties, and seventies grieve the life they didn't live because they were too infatuated and distracted by the idea they had to be thinner before they could do what they really wanted. And to make matters worse, despite the amount of money, effort, and life they've devoted to their "battle with weight," they grieve the fact that their body is far bigger than it was originally before they had decided they needed to be thinner. But once you start the pendulum swinging between enforced food restrictions and consequential impulsive food consumption, it's very difficult to stop the cycle—especially when embarrassment and shame increases as you gain even more weight.

The worse a person feels about herself because of this struggle, the more rigid she'll approach diets. The stricter she diets, the more fragile she is to likely fail, and the more intense grows her desire to eat. Eventually, this cycle ends in more and more weight gain. Any person who lives this way is set up from the get-go to perpetually chase the conditions that are sold as "easy" ways to fulfill her desire to feel lovable, included, and to belong. And even if she does reach the ideal body image, the freedom doesn't exist due to the continued effort, energy, and devotion necessary to maintain conditions that threaten food and aren't naturally sustainable.

If it took a form of starvation to be thinner, typically it will take continued starvation to sustain being thinner.

Ultimately, even when the fantasy body image is reached, and security in a thin-supremist culture is earned, the attack to one's access to food will have to continue, and survival impulses to eat will remain. Eventually, food will need to be eaten to stay alive, and weight will be regained. The cycle between dieting, weight loss, emotional eating, and weight gain goes around and around and around. The only way for this cycle to stop is to die or to surrender any dieting, and ultimately to surrender the ideal thinner body image.

There is an order to this process, which is:

1. In order to reduce the impulses to overeat, you'll need to stop judging food as either "good" or "bad" and restrictions of forbidden food will need to be removed.

2. To surrender all of food judgments and restrictions, you must accept the truth of your body without those controls.

3. To accept the truth of your body, you must accept the truth that others might and will judge, criticize, and dismiss you. *You will be put down and excluded.*

4. To allow for judgment and exclusion, you will need to verify and validate for yourself the worth you inherently bring to life.

To do this you'd have to secure your sense of worth, lovability, and your need to belong without a body image.

Independence: Can You Take Care of Yourself?

Maslow's third hierarchy of need *to feel lovable* and belong is far more complicated and complex than the first and second more important and stronger needs that are required for life. The third hierarchy of need isn't essential to stay alive like food is, but it has evolved as a need that is vital and has great impact on our emotional wellbeing. Access to food and shelter is straightforward, whereas relationships with others is vulnerable to 1) your ability to take care of yourself, 2) how you feel about yourself, and 3) how others feel about you.

Securing this hierarchy of need relies heavily on our own perception of personal worth, as well as our sense of capacity to survive if we are left on our own.

If you could independently adapt to challenge and find a way to provide your own needs, chances are you'd be less impacted by negative criticism than someone who is highly dependent on others to survive. And when you experience judgment and criticism, with a personal sense of worth, you're less likely to be triggered into self-defense, *or take it personally.*

A sense of personal capacity to adapt and learn skills necessary to take care of oneself is described as competence. Competence is what drives the energy and aptitude necessary to teach oneself, or to figure out how to make it on your own. Without competence, a person's need for assistance goes up. If that help comes from other people, your need to "fit in" and receive validation would increase.

> **When dependent on others, feeling unwanted, unneeded, un-appreciated, without value, lonely, or without something to give, would justifiably elicit emotional triggers of life-or-death stress.**

Without personally securing one's "self" first, symptoms of survival mode, such as anxiety, competition, paranoia, perfectionism, and the pressure to perform, would drive much of the mental state and work of an individual. But, as these survival emotions might increase productivity and willingness to conform, it also might increase emotional tension between one's mind and other members of her community.

In order to fulfill Maslow's *third hierarchy of need to belong,* it's not a matter of getting rid of the primitive sensitivity to being rejected and abandoned, but rather bypassing it with self-competence, using courage and grace to be real with oneself and others. This is true even when it's inevitable that others might not like or approve of you *if you don't conform to their needs.* It's not that you shouldn't "fit in," and adapt to your environment, but that you don't define yours or other's worth based on that ability.

This complex hierarchy of need is satisfied by two simple solutions:

1) To develop competence in one's ability to independently adapt and provide for him or herself, and

2) To perceive from within that he/she is integrally lovable and deserving of love, even if she/he makes mistakes, isn't the best, or might actually be the weakest, dumbest, ugliest, or worst person for the job.

In order to securely fulfill the third hierarchy of need, without it being vulnerable to outside opinion, you'd need to determine, *for yourself,* that you are worthy of love and belonging, even if others, including loved ones, don't agree—and even if you don't meet the ideal standards or "fit in."

Taking Ownership of Your Life

One issue stemming from the survival need to feel worthy of love, acceptance, and inclusion, is that as we are children, it is wired in us to give this security to our parents, family, and friends to validate. As we get older, we sometimes give this security away to a spouse, a career, or to a cultural belief system. Eventually, as we suffer trying to prove ourselves as "good enough," there comes a point, where in order to free ourselves, we have to reclaim ownership of our worthiness.

Over a lifetime of seeking to please others and looking for validation outside of ourselves, we can lose touch with who we are and can fear the truth of what we want in life. For many people it takes horrendous suffering before they are willing to surrender everything they know, to open themselves up to the fear they've attached to being the rightful owner of their life. The questions they come to ask is:

✓ Who am I?
✓ What do I want with my life?

To answer these questions, you must look inward to acknowledge and accept the truth of your thoughts and feelings, even though people you love might not agree. You'd have to be willing to honor your truth, even when family and friends might disapprove of you.

Only you have access to the integrity of the life you feel and witness on the inside. This is the space of life that you are experiencing and only you are aware of. If you aren't willing to face your own witness of life and recognize its truth, validity, and worth, and aren't willing to express it, how can you expect someone else to do it for you? How can others have a sense of who you truthfully are if you don't value it or use it?

> **You'd have to be willing to express the integrity you feel inside in order for others to recognize it. In other words,** *it is impossible for others to approve of you and your life if you don't approve of you or your life first.*

There is not one human being that has ever existed who can get into your personal life space, and know what you need, when you need it, to what degree, and to what intensity—*not even your mother.*

In order to fulfill this survival need, you alone are responsible to determine if you are intrinsically worthy of love and inclusion, even if you are extrinsically flawed and inadequate.

Ask Yourself:

- ✓ What's wrong with being innocently flawed?
- ✓ Why is being inferior such a bad thing?
- ✓ If you are in truth inadequate, not as good, or not the best, are these things worthy of shame?
- ✓ If you could accept this truth, would you feel free?

When you've developed a sense of competence, as well as fulfilled your sense of worth by accepting your natural and inherent truths, positive or negative opinions don't make or break the security needed to fulfill the third hierarchy of need to belong—specifically if you aren't afraid of your truth of being viewed as inferior. In that case, *no one's opinion really matters.*

Message from a Woman in her 30s after a consultation:

I just wanted to let you know how thankful I am for our session. It has made a huge impression and I still think about something you said: "You are afraid that everyone will find out that you are a piece of shit without being thin." It is so true, and seeing this has helped me understand my obsession with my weight. You helped me see that this wasn't a choice I made consciously, but something I used to pro-tect myself.

Thank you for showing me that I don't have to be angry at people pushing weight loss, diets, or body image. As you said, becoming "anti-religion" or "anti-fitness" or "anti- diet" is another way to be a victim and it won't help me to be free. I am at that point in time in my life that I am ready to accept myself. I don't want to resist any more because I want to be free from it all. For the first time I feel like I can be happy with my life, and there's nothing that needs to be done! I am so thankful for being able to feel free. The other day I ate a hamburger, and I didn't obsess about it or want to binge. Honestly, I forgot about it, which is incredible. This is a miracle, Robin. I think what you're doing is absolutely amazing. You saved my life.

Readers: What part of her experience resonates with you?

1. Are you afraid to be exposed as weak, inadequate, or inferior?
2. Are you seeking to fix your body to prove you aren't inferior, or worthless?
3. Do you resent the weight loss industry for selling you a body image and weight loss methods that have negatively hurt your life?

---

4. If you want freedom from your body, weight, size, dieting, and food from controlling your life, does it makes sense to play the victim or to resent the weight loss and diet industry?
5. What would it be like to eat food without thinking about it or having it make or break your day?

In Conclusion

In search of the truth…question the way you think and what you're afraid of.

Most of what I do with people when they seek my help is to give them perspective. I'm doing nothing other than giving them a different vantage point to look at why they're doing what they're doing, so they can understand what they'll need to give up and let go of in order to be free from the behaviors they want recovery from.

Besides discussing theories on survival mode, Maslow's hierarchy of needs, evolutionary psychology, narcissistic cultural dogma, body image, and thin supremacy…I spend a great deal of time asking clients clarifying questions.

I know for me, when I believed the misery of my eating-disorder behaviors were inescapable, and subsequently I decided to end my life—as I prepared for suicide, there were questions that came to my mind. These questions specifically exposed and unraveled my eating disorder as I sought to answer them truthfully—even if the truth challenged my beliefs and my identity. My answers came from a place of humility, seeking understanding rather than a way to defend myself or hide the disordered-eating behaviors. Today, I try to do the same when I ask questions of the person who is seeking the same clarity.

However, at first some people give me answers that are based on impulse, based on their fears, and based on their brainwashed dogma. In those cases, I refuse their answer, because they aren't telling the heartfelt truth. Sometimes I have to ask the same question 2–5 times, before a person actually thinks deeper and gives a truthful answer. When she gets past the mentally constructed answer, to seek the truth from her heart and soul, she experiences what it feels like to be humble, to be vulnerable, and to be free from aspects of dogma. *The truth does set you free.*

If you are wanting freedom from beliefs that shame you, behaviors that hurt you, and dogma that controls you, *ask yourself the questions you don't want to answer.*

Be honest even if it hurts your fearful ego. Look at your life from a viewpoint that isn't comfortable. Have courage to tell the truth, to be alone if that's what the truth entails, and to take responsibility for navigating and directing the life you are living in a way that brings you joy. When you open yourself up to the truth, you are opening yourself up to forgive yourself, to forgive others, and to forgive the rigid rules that keep you confined. You forgive your own humanness. Living in grace with the truth gives you freedom and a life you will feel worthy of living.

"Don't wait until everything is just right. It will never be perfect. There will always be challenges, obstacles and less than perfect conditions. So what. Get started now. With each step you take, you will grow stronger and stronger, more and more skilled, more and more self-confident and more and more successful."

– Mark Victor Hansen, author

Acknowledgments

I'd like to thank all the clients I've coached over the years who were willing to share their stories to the world on my YouTube channel. You are helping others by allowing them to witness your struggles and success in the process of recovery.

Next, I'd like to acknowledge and thank my copy development and line editor, Connie Anderson of Words and Deeds, Inc. Without her talents and the integrity of her work, I would have never finished this project, and it would've been far more difficult to read. Connie has been an imperative partner in capturing for the reader what I am trying to communicate. She is incredibly gifted and has been an essential influence to this body of work. Many people had told me that I'm a good writer—but my response is to let them know I have an incredible editor.

A special thank you to Denise Watson and Dr. Ed Hagen from Vivify Integrative Health in Hudson, Wisconsin. You gave me the opportunity to teach your patients, one by one, for years. Repeating the same explanation over and over, hundreds of times, was an invaluable part of refining how I teach the Mind:Body Method to participants. This work with you has been precious.

Thank you to my professors at Boise State University. Without such rigorous educational standards, I couldn't have understood the research that provided the basis for the content discussed in this book. To the Kinesiology department: Thank you for having such passion for the health of the human mind and body.

My hard-working and humble parents—for being the ultimate examples of perseverance and integrity. To sister Katie for your incredible artistic mind, and for the book title and cover design. To her and all my other siblings—Steve, Laura, Daniel, Jennalee, Debbie, Becky, Melissa, Cliff, Mike, Big Jeff, Little Jeff, and Jean—for helping develop my "character."

References

(1.) Sutin, A. R., Stephan, Y., Luchetti, M. and Terracciano, A. (2014). Perceived weight discrimination and C reactive protein. *Obesity.* 22: 1959-1961. doi:10.1002/oby.20789

(2.) Sutin, A. R., Stephan, Y., & Terracciano, A. (2015). Weight Discrimination and Risk of Mortality. *Psychological Science.* 26(11): 1803–811. https://doi.org/10.1177/0956797615601103

(3.) Sutin, AR., Zonderman, AB., Ferrucci L., Terracciano A. (2013). Personality traits and chronic disease: implications for adult personality development. *Journal of Gerontology Behavioral Psychological Sciences and Social Sciences.* 68(6): 912-20.

(4.) Engeln-Maddox, R. (2005). Cognitive responses to idealized media images of women: The relationship of social comparison and critical processing to body image disturbance in college women. *Journal of Social and Clinical Psychology.* 24(8), 1114-1138. https://doi.org/10.1521/jscp.2005.24.8.1114

(5.) Dittmar, Helga (2007). The Costs of Consumer Culture and the "Cage Within": The Impact of the Material "Good Life" and "Body Perfect" Ideals on Individuals" *Identity and Well-Being, Psychological Inquiry.* 18(1), 23-31, DOI: 10.1080/10478400701389045

(6.) Arjan E. R. Bos., John B. Pryor., Glenn D. Reeder & Sarah E. Stutterheim. (2013). Stigma: Advances in Theory and Research. *Basic and Applied Social Psychology.* 35(1): 1-9. http://dx.doi.org/10.1080/01973533.2012.746147

(7.) Andreyeva, T., Puhl, R. M. and Brownell, K. D. (2008). Changes in Perceived Weight Discrimination Among Americans, 1995–1996 Through 2004–2006. *Obesity.* 16: 1129-1134. doi:10.1038/oby.2008.35

(8.) Ying-Hsien Chao, Chao-Chin Yang, Wen-Bin Chiou. (2012) Food as ego-protective remedy for people experiencing shame. Experimental evidence for a new perspective on weight-related shame. *Appetite.* 59(2): 570-575. https://doi.org/10.1016/j.appet.2012.07.007

(9.) Aubie, C. D., & Jarry, J. L. (2009). Weight-related teasing increases eating in binge eaters. *Journal of Social and Clinical Psychology.* 28(7): 909-936. https://doi.org/10.1016/j.eatbeh.2013.06.012.

(10.) M. Macht and G. Simons. (2000). Emotions and Eating in Everyday Life. *Appetite.* 35(1): 65-71. doi:10.1006/appe.2000.0325

(11.) Puhl, R. M. and Brownell, K. D. (2006). Confronting and Coping with Weight Stigma: An Investigation of Overweight and Obese Adults. *Obesity.* 14: 1802-1815. doi:10.1038/oby.2006.208

(12.) Pearl, R. L., White, M. A., & Grilo, C. M. (2014). Overvaluation of shape and weight as a mediator between self-esteem and weight bias internalization among patients with binge eating disorder. *Eating Behaviors.* 15(2): 259–261. doi:10.1016/j.eatbeh.2014.03.005

(13.) Pearl, Rebecca & Puhl, Rebecca. (2016). The distinct effects of internalizing weight bias: An experimental study. *Body Image.*17: 38-42. doi:10.1016/j.bodyim.2016.02.002

(14.) Puhl RM, Moss-Racusin CA, Schwartz MB (2007). Internal-ization of weight bias: Implications for binge eating and emo-tional well-being. *Obesity* (Silver Spring). Jan; 15(1):19-23.

(15.) Major, Brenda, Hunger, Jeffrey M., Bunyan, Debra P., Miller, Carol T. (2014). The ironic effects of weight stigma. *Journal of Experimental Social Psychology.* 51: Pages 74-80, https://doi.org/10.1016/j.jesp.2013.11.009.

(16.) Sickel, A., Seacat, J., Nabors, Nina. (2014). Mental health stigma update: A review of consequences. *Advances in Mental Health.* 12: 202-215. doi:10.1080/18374905.2014.11081898.

(17.) Laura E. Durso, Janet D. Latner, Anna C. Ciao, (2016). Weight bias internalization in treatment-seeking overweight adults: Psychometric validation and associations with self-esteem, body image, and mood symptoms. *Eating Behaviors.* 21: 104-108. https://doi.org/10.1016/j.eatbeh.2016.01.011.

(18.) Lenny R. Vartanian, Alexis M. Porter (2016). Weight stigma and eating behavior: A review of the literature. *Appetite.* 102: 3-14. https://doi.org/10.1016/j.appet.2016.01.034.

(19.) Luchetti, M., Barkley, J. M., Stephan, Y., Terracciano, A., & Sutin, A. R. (2014). Five-factor model personality traits and inflammatory markers: new data and a meta-analysis. *Psy-*

choneuroendocrinology. 50: 181–193.
doi:10.1016/j.psyneuen.2014.08.014

(20.) Schvey, N. A., Puhl, R. M. and Brownell, K. D. (2011). The
Impact of Weight Stigma on Caloric Consumption. *Obesity.*
19: 1957-1962. doi:10.1038/oby.2011.204

(21.) Schvey, Natasha & Puhl, Rebecca & Brownell, Kelly. (2014).
The Stress of Stigma: Exploring the Effect of Weight Stigma
on Cortisol Reactivity. *Psychosomatic Medicine.* 76.
doi:10.1097/PSY.0000000000000031.

(22.) Seacat, J. D. & Mickelson, K. D. (2009). Stereotype Threat and
the Exercise/ Dietary Health Intentions of Overweight
Women. *Journal of Health Psychology.* 14(4): 556–567.
https://doi.org/10.1177/1359105309103575

(23.) Schwimmer, JB., et al. (2003). Obesity, insulin resistance, and
other clinicopathological correlates of pediatric nonalcoholic
fatty liver disease. *Journal of Pediatrics.* 143:500–505.

(24.) Carels, et al. (2009). Internalized weight stigma and its ideo-
logical correlates among weight loss treatment seeking adults.
Eating and Weight Disorders. 14(2-3):e92-e97.
doi:10.1007/bf03327805

(25.) Puhl, R. M. and Heuer, C. A. (2009). The Stigma of Obesity:
A Review and Update. *Obesity.* 17: 941-964.
doi:10.1038/oby.2008.636

(26.) Stone, O., & Werner, P. (2012). Israeli Dietitians' Professional Stigma Attached to Obese Patients. *Qualitative*

Health Research. 22(6): 768–76.
https://doi.org/10.1177/1049732311431942

(27.) Edelstein, Sari PhD, RD; Silva, Nicole MS, RD; Mancini, Lisa
BS. (2009). Obesity Bias Among Dietitians by Using the Fat
People-Thin People Implicit Association Test. *Topics in Clinical Nutrition.* 24 (1): 67–72.
doi: 0.1097/TIN.0b013e3181989af1

(28.) Puhl, Rebecca M., Heuer, Chelsea A. (2012). The Stigma of
Obesity: A Review and Update. *Obesity.* 17(5): 1930-7381.
https://doi.org/10.1038/oby.2008.636

(29.) Flint, Stuart. (2015). Obesity stigma: Prevalence and impact
in healthcare. *British Journal of Obesity.* 1: 14-18.

(30.) Geraldine M. Budd, Megan Mariotti, Diane Graff, Kathleen
Falkenstein, (2011). Health care professionals' attitudes about
obesity: An integrative review. *Applied Nursing Research.*
24(3): 127-137. https://doi.org/10.1016/j.apnr.2009.05.001.

(31.) Phelan, S. M., Burgess, D. J., Yeazel, M. W., Hellerstedt, W. L.,
Griffin, J. M., & van Ryn, M. (2015). Impact of weight bias
and stigma on quality of care and outcomes for patients with
obesity. *Obesity Reviews: an official journal of the International
Association for the Study of Obesity.* 16 (4): 319–326.
doi:10.1111/obr.12266

(32.) Anderson, Drew A., Wadden, Thomas A. (2004). Bariatric
Surgery Patients' Views of Their Physicians' Weight-Related
Attitudes and Practices. *Obesity Research.* 12(10): 1587-1595.
https://doi.org/10.1038/oby.2004.198

(33.) Geraldine M. Budd, Megan Mariotti, Diane Graff, Kathleen Falkenstein. (2011). Health care professionals' attitudes about obesity: An integrative review. *Applied Nursing Research.* 24 (3):127-137. https://doi.org/10.1016/j.apnr.2009.05.001

(34.) Bertakis, K. D. and Azari, R. (2005). The Impact of Obesity on Primary Care Visits. *Obesity Research.* 13: 1615-1623. doi:10.1038/oby.2005.198

(35.) Watson, A. C., Corrigan, P., Larson, J. E., & Sells, M. (2007). Self-stigma in people with mental illness. *Schizophrenia Bulletin.* 33(6): 1312–1318. doi:10.1093/schbul/sbl076

(36.) Rebecca M. Puhl, Jamie Lee Peterson and Joerg Luedicke (2013). Weight-Based Victimization: Bullying Experiences of Weight Loss Treatment–Seeking Youth. *Pediatrics.* 131 (1): e1-e9. https://doi.org/10.1542/peds.2012-1106

(37.) Aldrich, Tess & Hackley, Barbara. (2010). The Impact of Obesity on Gynecologic Cancer Screening: An Integrative Literature Review. *Journal of Midwifery & Women's Health.* 55: 344-56. doi: 10.1016/j.jmwh.2009.10.001

(38.) Satter, Ellyn. (2007). Eating competence: definition and evidence for the Satter Eating Competence model. *Journal of Nutrition Education and Behavior.* Sep-Oct; 39(5): S142-53 doi:10.1016/j.jneb.2007.01.006

(39.) Wilke, Joy. (2014). Nearly half in U.S. remain worried about their weight. *Gallup.* https://news.gallup.com/poll/174089/nearly-half-remain-worried-weight.aspx

(40.) Rideout, C. A., Mclean, J. A., and Barr, S. I. (2004). Women with high scores of cognitive dietary restraint choose foods lower in fat and energy. *Journal of the American Dietetic Association*. 104(7): 1154-1157

(41.) Carr, K. D. (2011). Food scarcity, neuroadaptations, and the pathogenic potential of dieting in an unnatural ecology: binge eating and drug abuse. *Physiology & Behavior*. 104(1): 162–167. doi:10.1016/j.physbeh.2011.04.023

(42.) Noa Zitron-Emanuel, Tzvi Ganel. (2018). Food deprivation reduces the susceptibility to size-contrast illusions. *Appetite*. Vol 128: 138-144.
https://doi.org/10.1016/j.appet.2018.06.006.

(43.) Hill, Andrew. (2007). The Psychology of Food Cravings. *The Proceedings of the Nutrition Society*. 66: 277-285. doi:10.1017/S0029665107005502.

(44.) Buss, David. (1995). Evolutionary Psychology: A New Paradigm for Psychological Science. *Psychological Inquiry*. 6: 1-30. doi:10.1207/s15327965pli0601

(45.) Gilbert, D. T., Pinel, E. C., Wilson, T. D., Blumberg, S. J., & Wheatley, T. P. (1998). Immune neglect: A source of durability bias in affective forecasting. *Journal of Personality and Social Psychology*. 75(3): 617–638.
https://doi.org/10.1037/0022-3514.75.3.617

(46.) Joseph E LeDoux Ph.D. (2015) FEAR: The Amygdala Is NOT the Brain's Fear Center, Separating findings from conclusions. *Psychology Today*.

https://www.psychologytoday.com/us/blog/i-got-mind-tell-you/201508/the-amygdala-is-not-the-brains-fear-center

(47.) Walter B. Cannon (1927). *Bodily Changes in Pain, Hunger, Fear, and Rage: An Account of Recent Researches into the Function of Emotional Excitement.* Harvard University.

(48.) Stephen B. Karpman, (2014). *A Game Free Life.* The definitive book on the Drama Triangle and Compassion Triangle by the originator and author. The new transactional analysis of intimacy, openness, and happiness.

(49.) Hawkins, David.R. (2018) Map of Consciousness. *Book of Slides (The Complete Collection)* Presented at the 2002-2011 Lectures with Clarifications. Pages: 12,104-107

(50.) Steven Bratman, (2017). What is Orthorexia? http://www.orthorexia.com/

After publishing *Weight-Loss Apocalypse* in 2011, author Robin Phipps Woodall started a YouTube Channel to share her coaching sessions that helped people who struggled to stop emotional eating. As Woodall met with each of her coaching clients, she found that her significant experience with an eating disorder, as well as her miraculous recovery, kept coming up in their discussions. For thousands of followers, Woodall's story was only understood through bits and pieces discussed in these YouTube videos.

In this book, Woodall tells how in the matter of a couple of years she went from being a cheerful college student to suffering with suicidal depression and a relentless eating disorder. While in a deep state of contemplation as she emotionally prepared to end her life, Woodall miraculously recovered. Not only did she experience an instantaneous removal from every negative aspect of the disorder and depression, but she also came out of it having a total shift in the way she perceived and lived life.

After over 20 years of being totally recovered, Robin Woodall is excited to tell you her story: *My Weight-Loss Apocalypse.*

After 8 years, author Robin Phipps Woodall has updated *Weight-Loss Apocalypse*, adding 52 pages of new mind-opening content. In the second edition, along with the important discussions of Dr. Simeons' hCG protocol, the need for further scientific investigation, and the hunger and fullness scale, Robin examines further the impact dieting has on emotional eating.

She explains: Until the influence that dieting has on over-eating or emotional eating is exposed as problematic, the demand for excessive amounts of food will continue, and weight gain will always be viewed as the problem. This additional discussion is instrumental in preparing the reader for the next book in the series: *Weight-Loss Apocalypse, Book 2*, which complements this book by addressing how body image negatively impacts how people approach Dr. Simeons' protocol.

For this reason, Robin is excited to present this updated second edition as *Weight-Loss Apocalypse, Book 1*.

"Robin has done it again. Whether you're new to the hCG protocol, or you've done the protocol more times than you'd like to admit this groundbreaking book is for you."

– Becky Sumsion, RDN, CD, Life Coach, Author

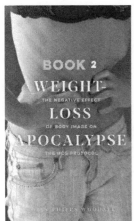 After over a decade of continued observation, author Robin Phipps Woodall is excited to share what she's discovered regarding the emotional impact of Dr. Simeons' hCG protocol. In *Weight-Loss Apocalypse– Book 2*, Robin examines the affect that negative body image has on a person's impulse to diet—and how repeated cyclical bouts of the hCG protocol done for this reason can be emotionally and physically harmful. Disarming beliefs that impel people to feel bad about their body is an essential step when approaching the hCG protocol, not as a diet, but as a serious medical treatment.

In this book, Robin describes the psychological risks of the very low-calorie protocol as well as the importance of an emotional evaluation, alongside a physical evaluation, in determining whether a person is an appropriate candidate for the hCG protocol.

For thousands of years, cultures have pushed physical ideas and concepts of the body as a way for people to achieve superiority and success. Like foot binding to make feet smaller, or the use of corsets to minimize waist size, many of these body images result in painful disability and disfigurement. Today the "superior" body being pushed comes from ideas of health and attractiveness as seen through images of ultra-lean thinness. Author Robin Phipps Woodall calls this "the culture of thin supremacy."

In *Thin Supremacy*, Woodall connects the individual's drive to achieve superior body images to human survival instincts, compelling people to fit in as a way to be viewed as worthy of love and inclusion. Unfortunately, as images of worth based on thinness have become more and more unrealistic, sadly this is on the rise: people suffering from emotional issues stemming from shame about their body. Woodall confronts the culture of thin supremacy—and encourages the reader to question their beliefs about body image.

In this book, author Robin Phipps Woodall builds on the significant discussion of body image from her first book, *Thin Supremacy*. Here she expands further to explore the overwhelming—and sometimes traumatic or even tragic—impact that negative body image has on dieting and emotional eating.

From the viewpoint of evolutionary psychology, in *Diet Supremacy*, Woodall illustrates how fears of social stigma, based on body fat, trigger primitive survival mechanisms that motivate people to seek safety and control through forms of "diet supremacy." The toxic bond between negative body image and dieting while surrounded by abundance of food, promotes the angst and strain responsible for increasing one's feeling of deprivation. The result is an increase in cravings, perceived hunger, and the impulsive drive to eat excessively. This is an important topic every weight-loss business, dieter, emotional eater, and eating disorder specialist needs to know about, understand, and especially discuss with those affected.

In *Body Supremacy*, author Robin Phipps Woodall expands on her first book, *Thin Supremacy*, and her second book, *Diet Supremacy*, to describe how these narcissistic belief systems combine to form the foundation for an eating disorder to develop. From the perspective of her own amazing recovery, Woodall presents a discussion about eating disorders as a psychological syndrome stemming from mechanisms of survival. A person suffering with an eating disorder is fighting to survive, even though her defense mechanisms are in fact killing her.

This book would interest a reader who wants to study and understand a different point of view for why people hold themselves hostage inside the darkness of an eating disorder. If you are studying eating disorders, work with people who suffer inside the darkness of an eating disorder, or are suffering yourself, this most-informative book was written for you.

In *Life After Supremacy*, author Robin Phipps Woodall describes the perspective of living your life while coming out of the self-centered nature of survival mode that was previously controlled by "thin and diet" supremacy belief systems. When a person rejects those belief systems to instead accept herself unconditionally, survival mechanisms calm down, and her mind shifts open. As people are liberated from narcissistic body images and diet supremacy, they are left to question how they should eat moving forward.

For this reason, Woodall describes in *Life After Supremacy* the science of hunger and satiety, as well as how important these physical senses are when relearning how to eat without fear or shame. The goal is to renew your relationship with your body and food in such a way that they are not the focus of your life as you move forward. This leads to the glorious and life-saving freedom people experience when they are recovered.

FOR MORE INFORMATION

Website: *https://weightlossapocalypse.com*

Email: *info@mindbodyhcg.com*

YouTube: *https://youtube.com/user/weightlossapocalypse*

Instagram: *@WeightLossApocalypse*

Twitter: *@MindBodyMethod*

Facebook: *Weight-Loss Apocalypse*

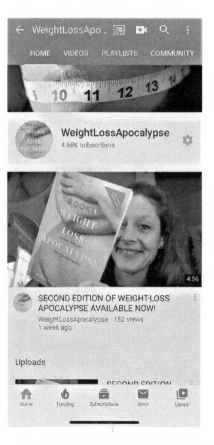

Made in the USA
Columbia, SC
01 July 2021